ORGANIZATIONAL BIOGRAPHY

The Directorate of Land Strategic Concepts[1] provides advice to the Chief of the Land Staff on the future security environment, the capabilities that will be required to operate in that environment, and alternative concepts and technologies to achieve the required capabilities. In meeting its mandate, the Directorate examines a wide range of issues covering the global and domestic environments, emerging technologies and allied and foreign force developments. The future army team consists of a small group of military personnel and civilian defence scientists supported by a wide range of contacts, both military and civilian, both Canadian and international.

[1.] http://armyapp.dnd.ca/dlsc-dcsot/

CRISIS IN ZEFRA

CRISIS IN ZEFRA

Directorate of Land Strategic Concepts

Department of National Defence—Director General Land Capability Development Kingston, Ontario, Canada—2005

All rights reserved.

Cover Illustration: Kalman Andrasofszky

Story Author: Karl Schroeder

Interior Art: Kalman Andrasofszky

Design: Army Publishing Office, Kingston

National Library of Canada Cataloguing in Publication Data

DND

Crisis in Zefra

Includes bibliographical references and Index.

ISBN D2-172/2005E 0-662-40643-5

NDID B-GL-007-000/AF-001

1. DND 2. Canada. Canadian Armed Forces—Fiction

"I thought I was a well-trained man for war when I landed here. Boy I learned about fighting, and learned that I didn't know much. But I learned..."

General Jacques Dextraze, Chief of the Defence Staff

Reflecting on his experience in Normandy, June 1944

"The nation that will insist upon drawing a broad line of demarcation between the fighting man and the thinking man is liable to find its fighting done by fools and its thinking by cowards."

Sir William Francis Butler

TABLE OF CONTENTS

PREFACE

The Army is a vital component of the Canadian Forces, the key national security institution charged with the defence of the nation. Meeting this complex and demanding challenge requires constant preparation, logical and sustained evolution, and advancement with purpose.

Between 1945 and 1989 Canada's Army was focused largely on the cooperative defence of Western Europe. When the Cold War ended, however, the Army entered a sustained period of exceptionally high operational tempo as it conducted ops, and kept the peace in over a dozen countries around the globe. Places previously little known to the Army soon became household names. Kuwait, Bosnia, Croatia, Somalia, Rwanda, Kosovo, and Afghanistan emerged as the new theatres of operation from the 1990s forward to today. The current security environment and anticipated future security challenges demonstrate that our Army must be expected to operate anywhere, anytime, under any circumstances.

Today, the Army continues to prepare for the many new and increasingly complex global threats that are emerging. Part of this process is the exploration of Army future concepts and design studies employing diverse methodologies. Since the origins of Canada's professional Army, literary fiction has been a useful tool with which to engage in the illustration and debate of future concepts.

Crisis in Zefra builds on the Army's strong tradition of looking and thinking ahead. Although this book is set in a fictional location ten to fifteen years from now, already we are witnessing the threads linking today to this fictional—yet highly possible—vision of tomorrow. I invite you to read *Crisis in Zefra*, debate its concepts, and participate in building the Army of the Future.

Director General Land Capability Development

INTRODUCTION

Though there are many ways to illustrate and debate concepts for future warfare, perhaps no simpler and more straightforward method exists than that of literary fiction. As such, this tool has remained a constant favourite in the belt of future thinkers in western armies, and has been regularly employed to impart new ideas, valuable lessons learned, and to encourage debate on what might be the next step.

This latest publication, *Crisis in Zefra*, follows a well-established Canadian Army tradition of fictional narrative, the practice of which dates back well over a century. Conceived by the Directorate of Land Strategic Concepts and with the assistance of a science fiction author and illustrator, *Crisis in Zefra* was constructed with the aim of introducing possible future systems of command and control, new technologies and post-modern tactics, techniques and procedures. At the same time, *Crisis in Zefra* may appear eerily familiar to some; the sense of familiarity is intended to keep the story plausible while exploring the not yet possible. Most importantly, the story is intended to introduce but one of many concepts of how Canada's Army may fight its future wars, with the hope that the reader will deconstruct, analyze, and debate the ideas presented here.

Much is said about Army transformation, but in order to remain relevant and successful, the Army must relentlessly reassess itself as an institution and explore new options. As the security environment continues to mutate, it is our duty to ask "what if?" and constantly explore alternative futures, any one of which might become a reality for us down the road.

In 2003, the Directorate of Land Strategic Concepts published Future Force,[2] a theoretical conceptual framework designed to assist the Army leadership and those staffs working on the Army of Tomorrow constructs. It describes an outlook and trends that reach out to 2025 and it provides recommendations to allow the Army to evolve to meet and conquer the challenges it will face in the future.

Crisis in Zefra is designed to act as a follow-on to *Future Force*, putting some "meat on the bones" of the ideas explored in that publication. Readers should note that the discussion/lessons sections at the end of each chapter are designed to complement Part I of Future Force. Readers are encouraged to consult that publication as they read and debate the ideas

---

[2] http://armyapp.dnd.ca/dlsc-dcsot/docs/FPAC_eng.pdf

and issues raised throughout this work.

Most importantly, I ask that you think about the Army of the future, debate its concepts as illustrated here, and let us know what you think. Your input is critical to our success.

Director Land Strategic Concepts

CAST OF CHARACTERS
(In order of Appearance)

Ebun Ishangi—DND Civilian strategic analyst, translator and specialist, East African region

Raymond Torretti—Foreign Affairs Canada strategic analyst, East African region

Sergeant Leslie Campbell—Section Leader. LIDAR Patrol Commander, South-eastern Quadrant, Zefra City

Corporal Michel Marchand—Patrol member

Corporal Arnold 'Daz' Blackmore—Patrol member

Corporal Marcie Tam—Patrol member

Warrant Officer Vadna Desai—Operations Warrant Officer (Ops WO), Headquarters Canadian Task Force Zefra (HQ CTFZ)

Mastan Nouria—Leader of the Zefra cell of the Fanonist Irredentist Fellaheen (FIF)

Idris Kabadi—Nouria's second-in-command

Major Monet—Operations Officer, HQ CTFZ

Martin Hutchinson—Intelligence Officer, National Defence Operations Centre (NDOC)

Suah—Local boy, Zefra City

PART I
UNDER THE WHITE TOWERS

~

Her minder[3] beeped again. Ebun Ishangi ignored the computer[4]; the taxi was already passing the bomb sniffers[5] outside the National Defence Headquarters (NDHQ) Ottawa building. Whatever it was this time, it could wait the minute or so it would take her to get through the building's multiple security layers[6] and reach NDOC.

It had been odd, this silent drive through the empty pre-dawn streets of Canada's capital. April snow lay piled everywhere, but the sun would be hot today; the Rideau was dark and clear of ice, but the news on the radio still talked about ice-fishers stranded on Lake Simcoe. In winter, Ottawa resembled the illustrations in the book of Russian fairy tales she'd owned as a girl; in the summer it was a green parkland with isolated towers poking up here and there through the foliage, a city overtaken with green like the abandoned London of H.G. Wells' *The Time Machine*.

In April, at night, it balanced between two worlds, like no place she had ever seen. Black and quiet, like a seed erupting. The faces visible at donut shops and gas stations were closed and private, conversations inaudible. Yet every few minutes her minder[7] would beep again, a tiny cry of alarm that signalled that somewhere, something had gone wrong.

Because they had called her, that "somewhere" was in Africa.

She stepped out of the driverless cab[8] in a swirl of black-and-red skirts. A mud stain decorated the hem from a puddle she'd stepped in on her way out of her apartment building. She didn't bother to examine how well she'd cleaned it but briskly strode through the glass doors of NDOC, her hesitation barely perceptible as they verified her identity: Ebun Ishangi, translator and specialist[9], East African cultures. Recently, Canadian citizen. Always, a deep vessel of memories of the sun-blasted and abject continent from which she had escaped.

[3.] http://www.newsfactor.com/story.xhtml?story_id=31342

[4.] http://www.mobilemag.com/content/100/102/C2622/

[5.] http://www.sciencentral.com/articles/view.php3?language=english&type=24119&article_id=218391158&cat=3_3

[6.] http://www.biometrics.org/html/introduction.html

[7.] http://www.pcmag.com/article2/0,1759,1612231,00.asp

[8.] http://www.time.com/time/2001/inventions/go/inbus.html

[9.] http://www.mcneilml.com/

Officers and staff criss-crossed the foyer; something was up that hadn't yet made the news feeds[10]. On the drive up, Ebun's eyes had flicked again and again to her customized news aggregator[11], which like a faithful dog had followed her from home, temporarily displaying itself on the screen in the back of the cab. She'd told it[12] to show her the latest from Africa—the only words spoken in the cab after she gave her destination. There was nothing, just a scrolling rehash of stale news. Into that absence, her imagination had begun to project possibilities.

She was just checking her minder into security when a familiar voice made her smile. "Ebun, there you are!" She'd always suspected that Raymond Torretti could be a friend outside work, but the Foreign Affairs analyst lived on Greenwich Mean Time[13] and she rarely saw him except when her job floated her into his department. "Sorry to call you in the middle of the night, but we need you on this one," he said.

She didn't ask what that meant; she had a good idea, but it wouldn't become real until the name was spoken. She would wait.

They passed through the second set of security doors into the NDOC working space. The building had been constructed during that quaint era when the concept of the "office" had been awkwardly married to early computer technology. Once subdivided into small rooms and large open areas full of cubicles, the interior of the building was now carved into various open circles[14] fronted by curved walls; people stood or sat around these, talking in small clusters or staring off into space. Scattered through the space were a few glass-walled meeting rooms[15] and many windowless cubby-holes. Ebun spent much of her time alone in those little rooms, staring at blank walls through augmented reality glasses[16] that made her believe, at times, that she was really back in Africa.

"Where do you want me to sit?" she asked, looking around.

"Doesn't matter," Raymond said. "The whole place is on this right now. It

[10] http://www.wired.com/news/infostructure/0,1377,63538,00.html

[11] http://www.disobey.com/amphetadesk/

[12] http://zdnet.com.com/2100-1104-5137597.html

[13] http://www.silkrc.com/Columns/BizXCulture/TimeZones.htm

[14] http://www.cs.unc.edu/Research/stc/

[15] http://www.glassresource.com/sub/special/privacy.htm

[16] http://www.ait.nrl.navy.mil/vrlab/pages/equipment.html

started this morning with a patrol," he added as he handed her a pair of the dark-lensed frames[17]. "It's been escalating ever since—?

"Morning my time, or your time?"

"My time," he said. She switched on the glasses, and the space around her came to life, full of virtual screens and windows, scrolling numbers, and menu reticles. The theatrical metaphor[18] of computer interface design had finally displaced the old "desktop" metaphor—at least here. Ebun still saw the old flat-screen devices in libraries and government offices. And they were all she'd known back home.

Back home . . . "It's happened, hasn't it?" she asked as Raymond led her towards one of the sunken areas where a crowd was standing and sitting around a virtual cloud of moblog[19] aggregators and status windows.

Raymond nervously scratched his iron-grey hair. "That's why I called you. We maybe could have gotten by without you—it's not that big a deal yet— but the place where it's happening . . . "

"Is mine," she finished grimly. They had reached the edge of the sunken oval, and it did seem like a theatre[20] with its largely seated audience half-surrounding a stage made of light, its virtual sets the very heat-wavering streets and washed out skies that Ebun had fled. And there they were, coming on line all at once through dozens of independent video aggregators[21]: the streets she had despised and tried to forget, the markets whose squabbling crowds invaded her dreams to this day. A vast, incoherent riot of humanity swirling for centuries around the white towers, standing for generations like an eddy in a fast stream; threatened now by the greed for oil and water[22] that had seized the entire subcontinent.

"Zefra," she whispered, and she didn't know whether it was a prayer or a curse.

[17] http://www.microopticalcorp.com/Products/HomePage.html

[18] http://www.astralsite.com/Drama/read3.html

[19] http://www.textamerica.com/mobinfo.aspx

[20] http://www.usatoday.com/tech/columnist/ccmak005.htm

[21] http://www.dada.at/blendobox/2004/02/10

[22] http://www.itt.com/waterbook/Wars.asp

❧

The sun had just risen but already the asphalt was softening in the heat. Sergeant Leslie Campbell looked down at where his boots had dented the surface of the Canadian Army compound's courtyard and shook his head. "Make sure that thing's air conditioning works," he said, "or we're gonna fry."

"Vehicle says it works[23],? said Corporal Michel Marchand from where he crouched next to the tires of the Mark II Camel assigned to the patrol. "Never known one to lie." He was changing a tire that the Camel's vetronics had said was fatigued. The tire looked perfectly good to Campbell, but Marchand's trust in his vehicles' opinions was absolute—to the point where he was the butt of occasional jokes on the subject.

"Might be too late for these little guys," said Corporal Arnold 'Daz' Blackmore as he sorted through the carton of inert swarmbots[24] in the back of the Camel. "Looks like somebody left them out in the sun a tad too long. Better get a new batch before we set out."

"OK, and make sure the dragonflies[25] are working," said Corporal Marcie Tam, the last member of the squad, as she handed Marchand a slightly less battered-looking auxiliary fuel cell battery[26] than the one now in the Camel. "Sure, you can spot the dug-up dirt of a mined road if you set your head mounted display[27] to highlight recently-turned gravel. But some people still use car bombs, even with the sniffer[28] technology. Forget air conditioning and tires, we need good drones[29] like these 'bugs'[30]?

Campbell ignored them all, leaning on the Camel's fender to take one last unmediated look at the shimmering rooftops of the ancient city, before putting on his head mounted display[31]. This one was terribly uncomfortable,

[23] http://www.ndia.org/Content/NavigationMenu/Meetings_and_Events/Past_Events/2003_Intelligent_Veh_3570.htm

[24] http://www.irobot.com/governmentindustrial/product_detail.cfm?prodid=33

[25] http://www.nationalgeographic.com/tv/explorer/exp031603.html

[26] http://www.fuelcellscanada.ca/tresearch.html

[27] http://www.darpa.mil/mto/displays/hmd/index.html

[28] http://news.nationalgeographic.com/news/2003/10/1001_031001_tntsniffer.html

[29] http://scmstore.com/english/robotic/biorobots/zona_robobiologica.htm

[30] http://www.wired.com/news/gizmos/0,1452,47879,00.html

[31] http://www.advancedvisualtechnology.com/

unlike the extremely comfortable set-up he bought for use at home; he often joked that HMD actually stood for "Head-Mangled Display.[32]" If only the military's procurement system could keep up with the latest innovations[33], he thought.

The houses and towers of Zefra rose in waves up several low hills, each wave a snapshot of a different time. The old town at the very center was of mud-brick and stone, its rooftops festooned with obsolete satellite dishes now rusting or turned into rain-catchers by industrious locals. Around that were the mosques and white-columned mansions of long-forgotten Ottoman conquerors, and ringing them the jarringly out-of-place manors and pubs of the British colonial era. Then the city sprawled out into an endless maze of concrete boxes and burnt-out lots, the residue of twentieth-century slums. Only at the edges was the city modern. Here, you could pour a foundation slab and erect a white fullerene and nylon[34] tent over it in a couple of days[35]; the tents were nearly bullet proof[36] yet translucent, but best of all cheap. Presiding over the sea of white triangles were dozens of windmills[37], which provided electricity in local grids and ran neighbourhood water purifiers[38] as well.

Campbell and his squad had been asked to have faith that this new Zefra represented the future. Zefra was an independent city-state; so were most of the large cities in Africa, since the collapse of the old colonial nation-states. With the population pouring into the cities from the devastated countryside, this was where the political power was concentrated anyway.

Zefra was about to host the first election in the region in years. The new leaders of the city would carry tremendous influence over Zefra and its extensive hinterland. Supposedly, the international coalition, which included the Canadians, would ensure the election happened with a minimum of violence. The new Zefra was expected to improve after that.

---

[32] http://virtualreality.physiol.ox.ac.uk/headfixed.html

[33] http://www.cesweb.org/attendees/awards/innovations/rd_honorees.asp?boi=1

[34] http://www.americanscientist.org/template/AssetDetail/assetid/28780/page/9;__Bk8

[35] http://www.wired.com/news/technology/0,1282,66872,00.html/wn_ascii

[36] http://www.discover.com/issues/aug-04/rd/bulletproof-fatigues/

[37] http://www.siemenswestinghouse.com/en/windpower

[38] http://crnano.typepad.com/crnblog/2004/02/green_nanotechn.html

[39] http://robotics.eecs.berkeley.edu/~pister/SmartDust/

Old ways meet new technologies in Zefra City.

Looking out at the sprawling expanse of the old city compared to this tiny neighbourhood of virginal white, Campbell couldn't find it in himself to be hopeful. Nothing planned had ever come out as expected here. The city had never stood on its own, but no conqueror had mastered the intricate tangle of alleys and side streets well enough to force Zefra into submission either. With each wave of conquest had come guerrilla cells that took advantage of the chaos of rooftops, water drains, and narrow alleys to do hit-and-run attacks on the invaders.

History was repeating itself. The international coalition was trying to restore order and sanity—and sanitation—and supposedly, the majority of the citizens wanted the coalition here. The problem was the vicious minority. So far the coalition troops had been billeted on the edge of town, venturing into the city only during the day. Campbell had seen all this in other trouble spots; how could you win the hearts and minds of a citizenry when you hid from them behind barbed-wire and walls?

He sighed and fitted the HMD to his head, then strapped on his helmet. The indicators in his peripheral vision signalled green, so he said, "Ops, C2 check, over."

Twenty meters away, in the top-floor headquarters of the Canadian peacekeeping contingent, Warrant Officer Vandna Desai saw a kind of virtual ripple of data packets spreading out through the smart dust[39] covering her three-dimensional display of Zefra[40]. "All systems green," she said.

"Acknowledged," said Campbell's voice in her ear. "Always good to know you're being watched from on-high."

She smiled; her own HMD was in fact giving her a view from far above the city. As Operations Warrant Officer, Desai was responsible for monitoring the situational awareness[41] for the patrols. The virtual city over which she watched was an amalgam of live data from an aerostat[42] hovering fifteen kilometres overhead, swarming sensors scattered throughout the streets and rooftops, and a three dimensional computer model of the city that was accurate down to a decimetre.

Campbell's communications weren't coming in by radio, but rather were being relayed through the sensor swarm[43], which itself used 4th generation

---

[40.] http://store.sharpsystems.com/product.asp?sku=2555920

[41.] http://www.darpa.mil/ato/programs/suosas.htm

[42.] http://www.21stcenturyairships.com/HighAlt

[43.] http://www.pcmag.com/article2/0,1759,1610203,00.asp

WIFI[44], infrared[45] (IR) and terahertz[46] waves to make interference or signal jamming—or triangulation—virtually impossible. Coupled with the augmented reality[47] and voice-recognition[48] built into his HMD, this system provided exceptional situational awareness and greatly simplified radio voice procedure.

Before coming here, Desai had known little about Zefra beyond its reputation as a trouble spot for Africa's ongoing water and oil wars. From her godlike perspective above the city, she already thought she knew it better than she'd known Montreal before leaving home. She could zoom through the model as if flying through the real city, penetrating the walls[49] of houses and garages, automatic system agents counting vehicles and foot traffic[50] as she went. Not all the city was open to her view, however; there were gaps caused by an earlier database crash. Hence today's patrol.

She checked to make sure that the patrol's orders had been sent to their HMDs during the command and control check. Aside from showing the flag, they included a LIDAR[51] sweep of the southeast quadrant of Old Town. Directions had already been downloaded into the Camel and its semi-autonomous follower vehicle[52]; in a very real sense, the soldiers were just along for the ride today.

The election was scheduled for tomorrow. So far, things had been calm at street level. The patrol's biggest job was to be a visible presence and reinforce the message that the coalition was here and ready to protect the people's newly established rights.

Campbell read the orders and nodded, a motion he knew would be relayed

---

44. http://www.wi-fi.org/OpenSection/why_Wi-Fi.asp?TID=2

45. http://www.infraredsystems.net/

46. http://www.darpa.mil/MTO/Terahertz/

47. http://www1.cs.columbia.edu/graphics/projects/mars/mars.html

48. http://www.wired.com/news/wireless/0,1382,47545,00.html

49. http://pubs.drdc-rddc.gc.ca/BASIS/pcandid/www/engpub/DDW?W%3DCA_NAME++PH+IS+%27DEFENCE+R%26D+CANADA+-+OTTAWA%2C+OTTAWA+ONT+%28CAN%29%27%26M%3D10%26K%3D518404%26R%3DN%26U%3D1

50. http://cis.jhu.edu/wu_research/tracking.html

51. http://www.lidar.com/

52. http://www.globalsecurity.org/military/systems/ground/follower.htm

back[53] to Desai as a confirmation signal. "Mount up," he said to his patrol. "We're going to the old town."

"At least there's some shade there," said Daz as he slammed the Camel's door.

The two vehicles, piloted and unpiloted, exited the base and immediately slowed to a crawl as they moved into the stream of foot traffic, bicycles, donkey carts and decrepit cars all heading for the city center. This was Zefra's daily commuter scene, a nauseating ordeal if you had to face without climate control. Campbell wanted to keep the windows and convertible top shut and the air-conditioning blasting, but accessibility to the locals was important, so he rolled down the window and nodded when an old man sauntered up next to the vehicle.

The man held up a paper-wrapped bundle. "Hello, hello," he said in a thick accent. "Spicy food, hot food, is good on hot day, yes?"

Daz stared at him incredulously. Next to him, Marchand was checking the Camel's bomb-sniffer[54] readouts. There was no sign of explosives in that little bundle, but it smelled strongly of curry. "I'm sorry, sir," said Corporal Tam, "but we can't while we're on patrol."

"I have web site!" The old man held up a sheet of e-paper[55] hung around his neck. The grimy square flicked through English, French and Arabic too fast for Campbell to read, but there was a recognizable website address persisting at the bottom.

"You sell your stuff on-line?" asked Daz. The old man nodded vigorously.

"Algiers, Tunis, even Paris! Nobody know where I am, with courier service it not matter. Rich people buy. Is exotic."

"Who'd a thunk it," Daz muttered. He'd spotted a clear area near an Non-Governmental Organization (NGO)–run vaccination station and now slapped the dashboard, a gesture the Camel understood[56] to mean "drive on."

"Nothing like a good courier service," commented Marchand as the old man disappeared behind them.

---

53. http://www.acm.org/crossroads/xrds3-3/haptic.html

54. http://news.nationalgeographic.com/news/2003/10/1001_031001_tntsniffer.html

55. http://reviews-zdnet.com.com/4520-6033_16-4205284.html

56. http://www.computerworld.com/softwaretopics/os/story/0,10801,73729,00.html

Two sunburnt, blonde women at the vaccination station waved as the patrol passed. Daz waved back (causing Tam to elbow him) but Campbell kept his eyes on the crowd. He was aware of being watched by dozens of people in that mass of humanity; the peacekeepers were relied on, but treated with ambivalence here. They could not always tell friendly from hostile gestures, and despite Campbell's alertness none of them noticed as a man leaning on a vegetable-seller's table pulled out his minder and punched a speed-dial number into its phone program[57].

⤳

"Here are the game levels[58]," said the aging programmer. He ducked his head to the men assembled around the battered old table as he waved a thumbnail-sized media chip[59] in their general direction. Once Mastan Nouria's minder beeped to signal receipt of the data, he practically ran from the room.

"I don't understand this," muttered one of Nouria's lieutenants. "Game chips? Minder phones? Why don't we just put a rocket into their compound and then storm the place?"

Nouria smiled. "Because we'd lose. Even if we took the place. After all, THAT's not the place we want to take, is it?"

There came another knock. Idris Kabadi, Nouria's second in command, poked his head around the door. "There was a message through the anonymous remailer[60]," he said. "They're on the move."

Mastan Nouria, leader of the Zefra cell of the Fanonist Irredentist Fellaheen, glanced down at his minder. It was unrolled like an ancient scroll[61] across the tabletop, and now displayed[62] a blinking icon confirming Kabadi's news. "Good," he said. "Esteemed colleagues, it is time for us to disperse to our particular tasks. From this point forward, we communicate by semaphore or remailer only. Presuming," he said to Kabadi, "that the loyal supporters of our cause are on the rooftops with their flags?"

---

[57]. http://techrepublic.com.com/5100-6255-1043593.html

[58]. http://www.conitec.net/a4info.htm

[59]. http://www.fujifilm.co.uk/digital/accessories/xdcard/index.php?flash=6

[60]. http://www.andrebacard.com/remail.html

[61]. http://www2.parc.com/dhl/projects/gyricon/

[62]. http://www.technologyreview.com/articles/05/03/wo/wo_hoffman

"They are, sir."

"And that's another thing," said the lieutenant who'd spoken earlier. "Flags? Why not just use the minders? They can't zero in on our position fast enough to—?

"But they can," said Nouria. "I've seen it done. And they can listen[63] in when you call someone, once they know who you are. No. We do this my way."

"But games[64], minder phones . . . "

"Are the appropriate weapons if you want to take a city these days. The old ways will not work."

He sat back, steepling his hands, as he stared around at the men. "I've been writing down the sayings that the locals attribute to the Koran," he said after a short pause. "Do you know that none of them are actually from the Koran?"

"What's that got to do with anything?" asked the sceptic.

"The point is that language rules us and we don't even know it. Fanon knew. And the internet, it's a giant market where only *their* message can be heard. The language of the internet is the language of the colonials.

"When we fought to evict colonials from our lands in past times, it was simpler. If they physically left our soil, we could go back to the way things were. They would have taken their ways with them if they'd left. Today, even if they leave, their technologies stay; worst of all, their internet and their TV remain. It no longer matters whether the people themselves leave. They can stay, who'll notice? It's their presence in our houses, in the minds of our children through the internet, through games and Western dramas, that is the real problem. They control us through the net, and its instant translation[65] of any message they want to send us into any language they want.

"You mustn't forget our strategic objectives in the midst of gaining our tactical target," he continued. He held up his fingers, and counted off the points. "One: water and oil must be ours. Two: the city must be on our side. Three: we must use both One and Two to restore Zefra's culture, by

---

031505.asp?trk=nl

[63.] http://www.allbusiness.com/articles/content/23787.asp

[64.] http://www.unrealty.net/vsmm99/

[65.] http://www.web-a-dex.com/translate.htm

ending the dominance of the internet-crazed foreigners." Abruptly he stood up and slapped his hand on the table. "Now, listen! Only number One— *only One!*—can be achieved using conventional weapons." He held up his minder, on which a splash screen for the popular game *Fire in the Gulf* was emerging from digitally-created smoke. "Two and Three will be achieved by using the occupiers' own toys[66] against them."

He stalked to the tower's door and opened it on bright sunlight. Nouria gazed out at the whitewashed roofs for a moment before closing the door against the heat.

"It's ironic that it is Canadians who are about to be killed," he said absently. "After all, it was their philosopher Marshall McLuhan[67] who'd said that politics would eventually be replaced by imagery. Today, we prove that adage."

The others had risen from their chairs, and Nouria waved them past, shaking hands and hugging each as they passed the doorway. When they were gone, he waited, listening to the sound of engines starting in the courtyard below. After the last vehicle rumbled away, he closed the door and returned to his minder.

In the dusty courtyard below Kabadi waved the last pickup truck out into the street. It's actually happening. He heaved a sigh, wiped his forehead in the oppressive heat, and glanced once at the white tower where his commander still sat. Then he pulled out his own minder and made a call.

"Achta? Have the children left for school yet? Well, go get them. I don't care. Pull them out. Today they stay home."

He snapped the minder shut, and frowning, went to close the gates to the small, oil soaked compound.

Twenty minutes later, Desai was frowning at her display. "This is odd," she muttered.

Major Monet looked up. "What?"

---

[66] http://www.simulation.com/training/Military_Sim/military_sim.html

[67] http://cnn.technology.printthis.clickability.com/pt/cpt?action=cpt&title =CNN.com+-+The+screen-age%3A+Our+brains+in+our+laptops+- +Aug+2%2C+2004&expire=- 1&urlID=11195935&fb=Y&url=http%3A%2F%2Fedition.cnn.com%2F2004%2FT ECH%2F08%2F02%2Fschool.internet

"Sorry, sir. It's just a small anomaly in the traffic patterns picked up by the agents."

Monet walked over. "Show me on the big board[68]."

Desai transferred her view to the large wall display[69]. Zefra rotated before them, the dust and heat-wavering air edited out to show the city as it never had been: radiant and perfect. The streets of the city rippled faint green, an abstraction that represented the daily comings and goings of thousands of people[70]. The Doppler[71] radar mounted on the Canadian aerostat[72] high above the city had recorded the movements of truck, bike and donkey for weeks. By now Desai's programs had a very good idea what a normal morning in Zefra looked like.

"It's all statistical," said Desai doubtfully. "But usually you have an outflow of children from these neighbourhoods," she highlighted an area near the downtown, "as they go to school, while the parents head off to work." It was just a flow of dots to the computers, but it was consistent day in and day out. "But today some of the flow's reversed itself—spreading out from this point." She pointed to a low building on the edge of the Imperial British sector.

"What's that?"

"A school, sir. Maybe it's a holiday?"

Monet shook his head. "If they knew it was a holiday, they wouldn't go to school and then come home again, would they?" He scowled at the image for a while. "Anything else?"

"Some vehicles radiating out from a central point, where they haven't before." She indicated a tower in the tangle of streets that was the old town. "I checked the archive[73]. Six pickups all arrived at this compound within the past two weeks. None went out until this morning."

"See if you can locate them." It could just be somebody starting a new

---

[68] http://www.afrlhorizons.com/Briefs/Sept01/IF0012.html

[69] http://www.stereo3d.com/projection.htm

[70] http://www.scr.siemens.com/smvp04/

[71] http://www.usatoday.com/weather/wdoppler.htm

[72] http://www.theregister.co.uk/2005/04/13/broadband_airship

[73] http://newsinfo.iu.edu/news/page/normal/571.html

business. Uneasy, but unsure why, Monet walked back to his desk. He sat down and stared at the city sprawling across the far wall. Then he nodded and tapped a key on his computer.

"I didn't know this was here," said Daz. He lowered the window of the Camel, letting in a blast of heat, and examined the marketplace that almost blocked the street ahead. The main article for sale in this part of town appeared to be refurbished truck fuel cells[74].

"The ground map's incomplete," said Campbell. "That's why we're here . . . and it looks like the LIDAR's on the job." Behind them, the glass and metal dome perched atop the autonomous follower vehicle was nodding up and down. The laser it emitted was invisible, but back at headquarters, Desai would be noticing the addition of windows and doors to her detailed city model. From now on, as they drove, the LIDAR would be building a nearly-perfect three-dimensional model of the streets and facades around them. Campbell had looked at one back at the base; eerily, the model included any non-moving humans, who were just objects as far as the LIDAR was concerned. You ended up with a dense wire frame model that included frozen featureless human shapes, like those ash-covered bodies he'd seen in pictures from Pompeii. Somebody had told him they edited them out of the versions they showed to the media; too disturbing.

Five meters ahead of the Camel, some children were laughing as they chased two palm-sized helicopter drones[75]. The drones were part of the Camel's standard kit; it would have been odd to see a Camel that didn't have one or two of them circling around it. These ones bounced up into the air, out of the children's reach, momentarily putting them too far from the ground to sniff out any nearby explosive devices. Campbell wasn't as confident as Tam about the little devices ability to find Improvised Explosive Devices (IEDs); but it was true that such attacks were rare these days. The very presence of the little dragonfly-like drones discouraged would-be attackers from trying to plant explosives ahead of a vehicle.

Given enough time, the patrol would supplement the LIDAR with internal scans of the buildings done using terahertz waves[76]. The outskirts of the city had been imaged that way. The plan was to eventually be able to support mission specific rehearsals of house-to-house combat in these simulated

[74] http://www.hydrogenics.com/products_strategy.asp

[75] http://www.freerepublic.com/focus/f-news/1059919/posts

[76] http://optics.org/articles/ole/7/9/5/1

environments[77] from throughout the entire city.

As long as the ability to do it didn't make it more attractive, Campbell thought in private moments.

"Move ahead," he said, slapping the dashboard. At least Daz had been right about one thing: there was shade here.

At the same time as a warning indicator flashed across his HMD, he heard a voice. "Patrol, be advised that the threat assessment has increased to level three."

The voice wasn't Desai's, but a Command computer. The same message would be flashing out to every other patrol simultaneously.

Daz was speaking; Campbell waved him silent. "What's up?"

"Recon shows heightened activity," said the computer[78]. "Be alert to friendlies leaving your vicinity and anyone else arriving."

Campbell frowned and turned to look behind the vehicle. Two sweating men were carrying a load of boards across the street amid the usual swirl of burkas and long modest dresses. Everything looked normal.

"Dismount," he said. "We'll take it on foot from here."

Sergeant Campbell reached for the door handle—

And back at Ops, Desai's eyes widened as the aerostat's profile signature software[79] found a match. "Sergeant," she began—

As the figure of a man holding a shoulder-mounted grenade launcher reared up next to a chimney—

And Campbell's HMD flickered. His eyes interpreted the flicker as a shape diving on him from the upper left so he instinctively ducked, and then there was light and noise everywhere and the dashboard came up and hit him in the face.

Desai spun in her chair. "Sir, we have weapons fire. It's the LIDAR patrol in Sector Four."

77. http://www.newscientist.com/article.ns?id=dn7130

78. http://www.aaai.org/AITopics/html/natlang.html

79. http://cgm.cs.mcgill.ca/~godfried/teaching/pr-web.html

"What's their status?"

"Direct connection is down, sir. Their suits[80] are going to have to build an ad-hoc network with the local smart dust. It could take a minute or two."

Major Monet nodded. The Camel's vetronics[81] weren't responding. The patrol's smartsuits[82] would compensate by pinging the nearest smart dust sensor, where it lay in evestroughs, alley or rooftop. The smart dust would use simple algorithms derived from ant behaviour[83] to locate a relay path back to Ops. Meanwhile, the patrol was on its own.

"What's their last video feed show?"

Desai called it up on the wall screen, while at the same time zooming in on the patrol's last location[84] using the aerostat cameras. The patrol's cameras showed a blurred picture of a silhouette on a rooftop; the frames advanced and it was obscured by smoke; then static filled the frame.

"Here's the aerial view." Desai put it on screen. "The vehicle is intact[85], sir!"

꙲

Everything was rattling around like dice in a cup and a swirl of smoke darkened Sergeant Campbell's vision. It came to him dimly that some gigantic sound had accompanied the rocking, but it all seemed to have stopped. Hopefully that was the sound-dampeners[86] in his helmet kicking in.

Campbell spun in his seat. "All around defence!" He could see the others clearly, but they were all faintly overlaid by abstract collections of coloured shapes: a transparent ball around the head, squares over the chest and rectangular boxes covering their arms. The enemy contact had automatically activated the tactical persona[87] that the HMDs provided to make threat-detection and enemy recognition easier. All the blocky shapes

---

80. http://web.mit.edu/isn/research/researchprojects.html

81. http://www.tacom.army.mil/tardec/vetronics/vethome.htm

82. http://web.mit.edu/isn/research/team07/project07_03.html

83. http://www.bath.ac.uk/mech-eng/biomimetics/about.htm

84. http://www.inertialengineeringinternational.com/inssystems.htm

85. http://www.dstl.gov.uk/pr/press/pr2002/01-07-02.htm

86. http://www.thetravelinsider.info/9nov2001.htm

87. http://www.evl.uic.edu/spiff/casa/

were green; the HMD was telling him that nobody's smartsuit had been penetrated or crushed by the explosion.

"Sergeant, your shoulder." Campbell looked down as he pushed the door open, and saw that the virtual cube surrounding his left shoulder was yellow.

Daz's voice had sounded deeper than normal and flat as if he were underwater; Campbell's earphones must be compensating for that ringing in his ears by shifting the frequencies of the squad's voices.

People were running to and fro as he hit the ground and crouched behind the Camel's open door. The HMDs were in full tactical mode now, so the running personas left trails behind them. Almost all of them were highlighted blue, which meant they were either facing away or moving away, or both.

The HMD had retained a memory[88] of the incoming grenade's trajectory. Campbell and the other three members of the squad could clearly see a fading red line stretching from the charred hood of the vehicle up through smoke and hovering dust to a nearby rooftop. He heard rifle fire now, but the sniper-detecting directional microphones were down, destroyed by the rocket-propelled-grenade (RPG) blast. He shouldered his CM29[89] combat rifle and fired back up the virtual red line as the others piled out of the Camel.

"Secure that entrance!"

"Which one?" It was Daz's voice.

He looked around and realized that Daz and the others had exited the vehicle on the opposite side. He could still see them, or rather their personas, as if the Camel were transparent. The HMDs still displayed the tactical personas and they knew where people were because they interacted with positional sensors[90] in the smartsuits. Campbell's own persona would also be clearly visible to the rest of the squad.

Now Campbell sat back and gestured with his hand[91]. A thin white line appeared in front of him and he grabbed at it. It wasn't a real object, of course, but another artefact of his HMD. His smartsuit interpreted the

88. http://www.computerworld.com.au/index.php/id;218358609;fp;16;fpid;0

89. http://globalsecurity.org/military/systems/ground/m29-oicw.htm

90. http://www.baesystems-gyro.com/News_MEMS_INS_GPS.htm

91. http://newsvote.bbc.co.uk/mpapps/pagetools/print/news.bbc.co.uk/2/hi/technology/3873481.stm

motions of his hand[92] and let him swing the line around, pointing it at the entrance to a building adjacent to the target's.

"That one," he said. "I'll cover you."

He set his rifle to automatic, raised it and fired. Behind him Tam was cursing.

"Heavy weapons are locked, Sergeant!" she shouted. Campbell glanced down at his rifle. Damn. All those blue icons had caused the patrol's weapons locks to kick in. Their side arms were operational, and the rifles would fire, but would not fire grenades or hyperbaric rounds unless Campbell overrode them. The locks were intended to prevent collateral damage in situations exactly like this one.

The patrol's heavier ordnance, mounted on the autonomous follower-vehicle, wouldn't work at all while the lock was in place.

His squad was in danger, crouched behind the thin cover of the vehicle. Before deciding whether to remove the lock, he had to put them in a position where they could go offensive. He stood up and started firing individual rounds at the rooftop. "Go!" Hopefully anyone up there would duck, or failing that choose him over his patrol as the better target.

The others rushed the entrance . . . and there was no return fire. Daz veered off to crouch behind another parked car. He waved at Campbell to make his own move.

Something crunched under Campbell's foot as he readied himself to run. It was one of the swarmbots[93] from the carton in the back of the Camel. "In ten, Daz."

He dove back into the soot-smeared vehicle. The damage looked far worse than it probably was; the Camel had electric armour[94] that discharged a tremendous jolt into any incoming armour-piercing ordnance. The result was a big external blast but no internal damage.

The swarmbots ' carton was intact. With it under one arm, he ducked and wove his way to the doorway while Daz laid down covering fire. There was no more return fire. Had this just been a hit-and-run attack?

"Sarge, are you hurt?" Marchand took the carton from him. Now Campbell

[92.] http://www.cybernet.com/~ccohen/gesture.html

[93.] http://www.wired.com/wired/archive/12.02/machines.html

[94.] http://www.dstl.gov.uk/pr/press/pr2002/01-07-02.htm

Coordinating attacks against Task Force Zefra.

finally had a moment to check out his shoulder; he tuned down the tactical persona and looked. The material of the smartsuit[95] was frayed and discoloured, some fine black fibres furring out around the seam. But he felt no pain[96], and the shoulder moved just fine. "Had my bell rung. Suit caught some shrapnel," he said, thinking that the material had probably saved his arm. "I'll reset its status to green."

∂

..."I'll reset its status to green," said a voice in Warrant Officer Desai's ear. She looked over at the major; he'd also heard. "Patrol back on line," she said anyway, and turned to review their status.

"RPG, sir. No casualties." She'd been pretty sure of that already. As the smoke had cleared around the vehicle, she had been able to watch through the aerostat's[97] cameras as Campbell's patrol ran for cover. The attacker himself had disappeared, leaving a spent launcher lying on a nearby rooftop.

All of Ops was moving into alert, and an auto-generated report on the attack was already available on the big wall screen. Desai checked the board, thought for a moment, then said, "patrol, our sims show a high probability that this is not a hit-and-run attack. We see possible hostiles converging on your position."

"We show a large number of civilians in your vicinity. Stand by for threat identification." Campbell nodded acknowledgment to Desai.

Desai looked back at the virtual Zefra display, and something immediately caught her eye. The aerostat's cameras showed several dots moving toward the street where the patrol was holed up.

Desai reversed time in her display and watched the group zip backwards and dissolve. All the figures had emerged form a street festival. She was able to zoom closely enough to verify that none of them were carrying rifles or larger weapons; but each held something to his or her ear, and had something else in their other hand.

"A number of young men and women are approaching your position," she said. "They appear to be unarmed mobloggers[98]," she added.

---

95. http://www.pcmag.com/article2/0,1759,1612232,00.asp

96. http://web.mit.edu/isn/research/team04/project04_02.html

97. http://www.sanswire.com/stratellites.htm

98. http://www.wired.com/news/wireless/0,1382,57431,00.html

"Video scavengers," said Monet. "This will be all over the world in five minutes."

A text-message from the patrol appeared on the big board. Campbell had used macros to send it using only a couple of taps on the keypad on the back of his wrist and several voice commands. The content was brief but to the point: a request that Ops send a quick-response team and explosive ordinance disposal (EOD) unit. A voice-to-text[99] message glowed underneath this request: "enemy is fortified on upper floor of a low-rise."

Desai tapped a key to send an acknowledgement to the unit. The major was leaning over her shoulder now, but as the Ops WO, it was her responsibility to manage the situation. "I'm going to pull up the database," he said. "I want to know if this attack fits the profile of the FIF."

"Good idea, sir."

"Have you started response simulations?"

"Yes, sir." To her relief, Monet simply nodded and backed off.

Desai fed the initial report into the internationally linked assessment network[100], and immediately a match came back. This attack was similar to another that had happened in Menaka the previous spring. The similarities included timing: both attacks had taken place at a crucial point in peace talks aimed at stopping local FIF incursions. Both had originated in crowded areas with lots of soft targets, and both seemed aimed at attracting immediate media attention.

"Looks like the FIF again, sir," said Desai. "Could even be the same guy who did Menaka."

"If so, then this is just the beginning," said Monet. "He'll be trying to start a general revolt."

He had to give an answer to the patrol. He didn't hesitate. "Let the patrol know that the quick response team is on its way," he said.

Mastan Nouria had his minder spread out on the table, and was reviewing the location news sites when Idris Kabadi burst into the room.

"They've made our position!" shouted Idris.

---

99. http://www.rapidtext.com/infosign.html

100. http://www.wired.com/news/privacy/0,1848,58936,00.html

Nouria stared at him. "You mean the patrol's position." He gestured at the windows open in the surface of the minder. Various web cam views around the city showed the international force's compounds. A small cloud of autonomous flying vehicles had just erupted from the Canadian compound, and its gates had swung back to disgorge several autonomous ground vehicles. The Canadian force was entering the maze of streets that led to the market, and the target patrol.

"No—look at the British!" Idris pointed.

Six armoured vehicles had pulled out of the British encampment. They were swinging onto a main road that terminated not far from this very tower.

"How do you know they're coming here?"

"One of the rooftop laser detectors went off. They did a LIDAR sweep of the whole building from that damned balloon. I don't know how they knew we were here—?

"Doesn't matter. Get ready to move out."

"Our location is compromised," Nouria gestured to a local boy who stood near the window. "Send a semaphore," he said. "Position compromised. Then get yourself out and meet us at the emergency rendezvous tomorrow." He folded up his minder, and he and Idris ran down the stairs. "What about Group Two?" he asked Idris as his second in command swung open the door to an old Toyota hybrid truck.

"The Canadians are still alive," Idris said tightly. "But we have them pinned down and the whole thing is being broadcast on phone cam[101]. Perfect timing."

"Yes but they should have been dead by now. We need a diversion to keep them from getting reinforcements," said Mastan. "Did Group Three place the bomb outside the aid centre?"

Idris nodded. "They paid some local boys to knock down the little bomb-sniffer helicopters circling the American embassy. The boys used a badminton racket, apparently. The aid center loaned the Americans its own sniffers, as we'd expected, so now they are vulnerable. But what good will bombing them do? They are all the way across town."

". . . Closer to the British, I know." Nouria unfolded the minder and calling up a city map, pointed to a snarl of intersections a quarter mile south of the

---

[101.] http://msnbc.msn.com/id/5092826/site/newsweek/

market. "This is where we're going to stop the Canadians."

"But we don't have anyone near there."

Nouria unrolled his minder. Images of Canadian soldiers firing into a raging mob flickered across its flexible surface."

Idris Abadi looked at the picture in surprise. "Where's that happening?"

"Nowhere—in reality. But all I have to do is upload this simulated scene created in the game engine, and we'll have a whole army."

"I don't believe this." Tam was looking at something in her HMD.

"What are you doing, corporal?"

"Sorry, Sarge, my minder's been surfing the news feeds while we've been . . . busy. It sent me an image it thought was important." She transferred the picture to Campbell's HMD.

The sergeant squinted at a virtual TV screen that appeared to hang about a meter away. On it was a miniature street scene that wobbled a bit. A tuft of smoke hung in the middle of the scene. "What the—that's here."

Tam nodded. "This just came up on the *Africa Today* news aggregator." Campbell leaned out cautiously to look down the street. Two young men were loitering at the mouth of the street. Both were holding up their hands, with small black objects just barely visible between their fingers. "Minder phones. They're videoing us right now."

Daz leaned out as well and waved cheerfully. On the virtual screen, a tiny grinning figure waved back.

Campbell stepped back and cursed. "What do you think the odds are that those guys just happened to hear the explosion and came to look?" he asked no one in particular.

Daz snorted. "As if." Marchand and Tam exchanged glances.

The initial confusion of the attack was fading. "If that's 'Fifi' up there, they're relying on the media attention," said Campbell.

"So?"

"So, deny them that and we deny them their objective."

Daz grinned. "Can I do it?"

"No. There might be political fallout later. It's my responsibility. You start pitching the swarmbots out there—and find out what happened to the drones. I'm going to use a chip killer[102], so set your suits and HMDs to safe mode and don't activate the swarm yet."

Campbell clicked a magnetic pulse grenade into the lower barrel of his CM29. From inside the stall he had a clean shot at the loitering cam-holders, while being protected from the sniper by the market building's stout walls and roof.

"Throw out the bots," he said as he lined up his shot.

Campbell's grenade traveled in an almost straight line; the CM29 was designed to deliver a grenade over a kilometre away if need be. He had programmed his to explode at a scant sixty metres. There was a small puff of smoke and a window cracked in the building next to the loitering youths, but other than that there was no visible effect.

Daz was practicing his baseball pitch with the bots, which were round and a bit bigger than golf balls. The few faces peeking out from the doorways up and down the street disappeared; they probably thought Daz was throwing grenades. But as Daz activated them each bot sprouted a blur of little legs and scurried in the direction of the sniper's building.

Moments later a solitary micro-helicopter drone buzzed after them.

Campbell spared a glance at the mobloggers. Both had dropped their minders and were now running away. A sensible reaction, now that everything electronic they had was fried by Campbell's grenade[103].

The sound of the gunshots changed. Somebody was firing a shotgun at the swarmbots. Several were hit but the swarm was robust enough to handle 50% casualties and still achieve mission success. "They're on-line and reporting," said Daz after a moment. Campbell turned to look; through the mud-brick wall of the stall, he could see the ghostly-superimposed framework of a building coalescing like smoke. The bots were hopping in through open windows and doors as the helicopter drone circled the upper floors. Some were getting stuck—apparently somebody had laid down double-sided tape below some of the windows. But every one that became stuck relayed its experience to the rest, who avoided the exact route it had taken.

[102.] http://www.abovetopsecret.com/pages/ebomb.html

[103.] http://science.howstuffworks.com/e-bomb3.htm

Non-combatant icons began to appear as the bots used Doppler radar[104] to locate human heartbeats and breathing. There were too many of them on the lower floors. As the bots registered gunmetal or smelled[105] explosives, several blue shapes near the entrance turned red.

"I see two enemy on the top floor and three in the stairwell," Campbell said. After a moment Desai said in his ear, "I have visuals. I confirm three enemy in the southern stairwell." Campbell imagined three men gaping into the camera and then hastily raising pistols to shoot the bot.

"Patrol, the men in the stairwell are in a defensive position and do not have a line of sight on your position."

This was the moment for one of those decisions he might regret later. Campbell remembered a previous tour of duty, in Pakistan, where the confusion of close infighting with civilians nearby had resulted in a storm of media criticism that crippled the mission. Policies towards weapons locks had changed, after that—but would he become a scapegoat anyway if non-combatants were killed today?

He sighed and unlocked the heavy weapons. Somewhere at headquarters an indicator would be flashing. Hell, somebody in Ottawa probably already knew what he'd done.

He'd worry about that later.

Turning to his waiting squad, he said, "okay, we're taking out that sniper. Tam, keep an eye on the street. Marchand, load up a clip of shrapnels and program them for . . . get a range on that window."

Marchand nodded. "Thirty-two meters." He and Daz dialled in the effects they wanted on their rifles' magazines. The liquid-metal-head[106] bullets could be adjusted to provide a variety of effects, but the sniper might not know they had them. After the weak gunfire he'd just seen, he might believe that a simple rifle was all he was up against. He was in for a nasty shock.

Marchand leaned out far enough to fire a volley of rounds into the open air, aiming at a point at roof-height next to the sniper's window. Gunfire echoes rattled up and down the street and Daz dove into the open, rolling behind

---

[104.] http://www.designnews.com/article/CA110182.html?stt=001&pubdate=01%2F19%2F98

[105.] http://www.sandia.gov/media/NewsRel/NR2001/watsniff.htm

[106.] http://www.newscientist.com/article.ns?id=dn4004

the car where he'd hidden previously. Marchand kept firing at the sky until Daz lined up his shot and fired off five rounds with clinical precision. He gestured for the others to advance.

Then he and Tam were out and running up the side of the street as Marchand peppered the target building with more cover fire. He now had a better view of the sniper's nest: an empty air conditioner cradle below a window. The surface of the wall around the window was peppered with thousands of tiny shrapnel craters from Marchand's airburst shots. Though his bullets exploded in mid-air, they obviously went off close enough to have shattered the window as well. Daz had then used his laser sight to aim at the ceiling of the room through the window; it was a simple matter to program the thermobaric rounds[107] to explode a meter shy of that ceiling.

The window was greyed by a dense smog that was starting to drift outside. Daz's thermobarics had sucked all the oxygen out of the room. Whoever had been in there was either sensibly gone, or unconscious.

Campbell tapped in the swarmbots' output, and saw that the men who had been in the stairwell had moved.

"They seemed to be taking up positions in a ground floor room."

Meanwhile, numerous human shapes—probably non-combatants—were hastily leaving the building's rear exits.

"We'll take out that room the same way," he said to Tam. "You—?

The whump was distant, its echoes overlapping the sound. But up and down the street, windows rattled.

Daz looked around. "What was that?"

Campbell shook his head. "Doesn't matter. Focus on the job. Ops, are the civilians all out of the building?"

There was no answer.

"Ops . . . ?"

&

"There was a line-up at the aid station," Raymond explained to Ebun as she lowered herself into one of the available chairs. She couldn't take her eyes off the scene of unimaginable carnage that hung, ghost-like, in the air before

---

107. http://www.wired.com/news/conflict/0,2100,58094,00.html?tw=wn_ascii

her. "Eyeball estimate puts the casualties at twenty," Raymond was saying; Ebun barely heard him.

I know that place, she was thinking. As a child she had gone there twice a week to receive food packages. The plaza that fronted the aid station had always been crowded, and she remembered it being defended for a time by UN troops. Now the place was a cauldron, its center a black tangle of still-smoking metal and bodies. They were almost all Westerners, she realized: the bomb had been carefully placed.

"The local coalition commander sent out a text-message within seconds to every person in the city registered as knowing first-aid," continued Raymond. "He smart-mobbed[108] a complete coordinated relief effort in less than a minute.

"This is a live moblog feed. The news aggregators have jumped all over it; it's the top story. There's already a buzz of theories on the discussion groups; they're blaming anti-election forces."

She shook her head, unable to tear her eyes away from the scene.

"Ebun?" Raymond put his hands on her shoulders, concerned. "We have another situation that we need your help with."

She snapped out of her horrified reverie. "Yes."

Raymond turned and gestured with one hand; the images of the market bombing disappeared. "What we need you to tell us," he said, "is what these people are chanting." And now into Ebun's earphones came a rising tide of voices, thousands of them it seemed in a musical waver of near-unison.

". . . Ops?"

"Acknowledged, patrol. Stand by for arrival of backup strikebots. They'll take care of that building for you."

" Acknowledged!" Behind the Major's crisp tones Campbell heard another sound. He wasn't sure whether the uneven roaring was local or coming through his headphones. Sir? I'm picking up a sort of sound—?

"Yes, patrol, we hear it too. It's coming in through the open window."

"But what—?

---

108. http://www.openp2p.com/pub/a/p2p/2003/03/13/howard.html

"That," said Desai on the other channel, "is the sound of a flash mob[109] blocking the streets between you and your relief force. The bots will still reach you because they're coming in by UAV. But as of right now, the squad vehicles are stuck in the crowds."

Campbell turned to his squad. "Looks like we're on our own—the bots, and us" he said grimly.

[109.] http://www.flashmob.com/

DISCUSSION

Future Security Environment

"Under the White Towers" reveals a future security environment where the Canadian Army continues to find itself engaged in an expeditionary role to assist in the stabilization of failed states. Given the nature of these missions and the increasing difficulty of simply applying a well-rehearsed mission template, DND has increasingly depended on its access to joint, inter-agency, multi-disciplinary assets and public (JIMP) resources and assistance in the execution of its tasks.

Some of the new and emerging concepts explored in this chapter include: multi-disciplinary operators; multi-Agency participation; cultural specialists; alternate cultural ideology; instant news reporting; and personal newsagents. Though arguably some of these concepts have existed previously in other forms, here their application employs new technologies in a network-enabled operation.

Consider the following questions (it is recommended that the Canadian Army publication *Future Force* be used as a reference):

1.   In the future, the Canadian Army will continue to deploy task force sized expeditionary forces specifically tailored for each mission, and should therefore organize itself towards this role. Agree or disagree?

2.   Command and control of future missions will increasingly depend on multi-disciplinary and multi-agency support. How can the Army increase its cooperation with such organizations?

3.   How will a future security environment dominated by clashing political, religious, and cultural ideologies shape the organization and roles of the Canadian Army in the future?

4.   Will the seemingly constant media presence in theatre alter the way in which a soldier executes his/her duties in the future? Will media reporting continue to have the same impact on operations in the future that it does today?

Emerging Technologies

This chapter introduces the reader to a 'typical' patrol in the Canadian Army of the Future. Forever a mix of the old and new, the following technologies are at hand:

- Software agents—AI automation
- Statistical surveillance and agents
- Vehicle automation
- Surveillance
- Computer interaction
- Autonomous situational awareness
- Playback/reach back
- Improved vehicle survivability
- Patrol weapon locks
- Smartsuits
- Insurgent databases
- Precision scalable weapons

Consider the following questions:

1. Should soldiers put their trust in autonomous systems for situational awareness at the tactical level? To what degree?

2. How might platoon and section level tactics be affected by the addition of autonomous robots within its order of battle?

3. Are patrol weapon locks helpful or harmful in urban environments? Who should have authority for release?

4. What information is critical to soldiers in a firefight?

The Future Battlespace

The future battlespace will likely see a continued Canadian Army presence in failed states and unstable international environments. Often required to operate in complex terrain, the following concepts are considered:

- Urbanization
- Ops simulations
- Local technologies
- Low-tech communications

- Low-tech response to high-tech

- Deception

- Smart mobbing

- Net enabled environment and the patrol chain of command

Consider the following questions:

1.   How accurate do you feel the depiction of this future scenario is? What, if anything, would make it more realistic?

2.   Do you think the Army will spend more or less time fighting in urban environments in the future?

3.   Do you see increasing threats from communications like cell phones, blackberry devices, and other PDAs?

4.   What is the value of training and preparing for operations using virtual environments, digital trainers, and even videogames? How does it compare to real-life training?

Allied/Adversary Developments

Both allied and adversary developments will affect the organization and culture of the Canadian Army of the Future. In this chapter the following issues were raised:

- Tactical Organizations—Future

- Technology and the procurement system

- Enemy tech capabilities

Consider the following questions:

1.   Given that Canada's Army may not be fighting large conventional formations in the future, how might it organize its order of battle to combat medium, small and asymmetrically organized adversaries?

2.   Would you prefer to receive somewhat effective technological upgrades right away for army weapons and vehicles or wait for fully effective solutions that may take longer to procure?

3.   What sort of technological threats do you think Canadian Army soldiers will face in theatres in the future?

4.   Will asymmetrical adversaries pursue low or high tech responses to

emerging Canadian Army capabilities? Why?

The Human Dimension

The human dimension of future warfare appears to remain constant regardless of changes in missions or technology. In this chapter the following issues were addressed:

- Abbreviated voice procedure

- Potential to eliminate voice traffic

- Hearts and minds

- NGOs

- Simplified contact reporting

- ROE against non-combatants

Consider the following questions:

1.   In the future, network enabled operations may mean that voice communications are further abbreviated and supplemented by automated commands. What is your level of comfort in receiving mission orders entirely from a computer rather than a human?

2.   Does the current reliance on voice or a mix of voice/data communication affect soldier's abilities to act quickly and/or decisively in certain environments?

3.   How will the presence of Non-Governmental Organizations affect future operations in an increasingly '3 block war' environment?

4.   In the future it may become increasingly difficult to easily identify adversaries in a theatre of operations. How might future Rules of Engagement address this challenge?

PART 2
RIPPLES

LIVE FEEDS[110]		
Free Sudanese Reporters' Guild	**BBC World News**	**National Coalition Council News**
"The Canadian soldier is raising his rifle. Oh God, he's firing into the crowd! I can't believe this is happening, but you can see it for yourself! We've got to do—"	"The Canadians are apparently using a radio-frequency device[111] to calm the crowd. It seems to be working; as you can see, the chanting has subsided, and a small group is talking to the troop's leader."	"No disturbance has occurred in the market this morning. I am panning my camera around the plaza, you can see it is nearly empty as the hot afternoon approaches..."

From Warrant Officer Desai's perspective, the thing had the quality of a slow dance—or like the swirl of a growing vortex in coffee being stirred. Zefra was on the move.

"It looks like coordinated movement on the ground, sir. Thousands of people are on the move. I've never seen anything like it." What she was seeing wasn't like riots, or even like the planned movement of troops. Crowds were coalescing in different parts of the city and moving purposefully towards key intersections.

"They're flash mobs[112], sir, that much we know. Each one is the result of a localized text-message appearing on the phones of the people in a particular neighbourhood. One message was religious, and said that Canadian troops had barged into a mosque—not true, of course, but it went out to a Muslim newsgroup and people poured into the streets near the place. Another said that somebody was trying to sneak a tanker truck full of water out of the city—that one tied up the main road. I'm trying to correlate the messages so far with their targets, to anticipate what groups might be flashed[113] next."

[110.] http://www.wired.com/news/culture/0,1284,64285,00.html/wn_ascii

[111.] http://www.au.af.mil/au/aul/bibs/soft/nonlethal.htm

[112.] http://www.abc.net.au/science/news/stories/s913314.htm

[113.] http://www.wordspy.com/words/flashmob.asp

"All right," said the major. "First, though, rewind the day[114] one more time, Warrant. I want to see[115] where those trucks from the tower went this morning."

In her earphones, Desai could hear the faint tones of the translator[116] who was interpreting for the relief troops. They usually got by with machine translation[117], but having someone with knowledge of local culture was always better. The woman, who wasn't physically present but "riding" the squad leader's HMD, said, "he's telling you that the price of water has shot through the roof, yet he claims your troops continue to get it for free. He's demanding fair and equitable distribution of water."

"Tell him his concerns are being heard," said the squad leader. "If he names a time and place for us to sit down and talk about the issue, we will be there. But right now he has to realize that some of our men in are in danger, and we need to pass." The translator's voice, electronically modified to resemble the troop leaders voice[118], issued from a loudspeaker on the front of the lead vehicle.

Desai turned her attention to the major's request. Since she had a full forty-eight hour buffer of indexed high-resolution video[119] from the aerostat to play with, she was able to back-step to the morning and locate the compound in question at dawn. Nudging time forward a bit, she located the moment when the trucks had left. As she had earlier, she tagged[120] each truck and let the pattern-matching software[121] trace their movements through the streets, until all had stopped. This only took a few seconds. As each parked, its icon changed color on a secondary map of the city[122] she had open in another window. This time, though, she tagged the small individual dots that appeared next to the trucks just after they stopped. These were right at the resolution limit of the system, because the total city

[114] http://news.thomasnet.com/fullstory/458461

[115] http://photographic.com/news/110504wearable/

[116] http://www.linuxinsider.com/story/36172.html

[117] http://www.eamt.org/

[118] http://www.surveillancedefense.com/c75.htm

[119] http://video.google.com/video_help.html

[120] http://www.rfidjournal.com/

[121] http://www.automationworld.com/articles/Products/897.html

[122] http://www.gis.com/whatisgis/whyusegis.html

feed wasn't zoomed in anywhere. Zoomed in, she could have told which men had dandruff. As it was, when she ran the pattern-matching software on the tagged dots this time, half of them promptly disappeared. They'd entered buildings, been swallowed in crowds, or simply wavered out of existence in the morning heat-haze.

There wasn't much information there, but there was enough. "Fully half of the men in those trucks disappeared into the city's industrial area. That's on the opposite side of town from all the action, sir. Four or five men went to the aid station, but they only stayed there a few minutes and then left. The rest dispersed into the neighbourhood where the patrol was hit."

"We need to isolate that area," said the major. "I want patrols here, here and here." Icons appeared at key intersections around the side street where Campbell's patrol had been ambushed, and tasking orders were generated automatically[123]. "But be alert to other indictors; I feel we're being drawn away from some sort of main event."

Desai called up the main situation map. With the flash mobs and projected positions of the rebels combined, it was clear that the city was being cut in two. The UN forces had concentrated around the aid station and the market, across town from the industrial area; flash mobs made a dotted line that blocked every intersection leading to that part of town. The coalition couldn't deploy non-lethal crowd control measures to disperse them, because each mob had a different motive[124]—some were protestors, but some were composed of people whose minders had told them of an unexpected sale on saris, or of the unannounced visit of a local video hero. Blasting away at such groups could ruin the hearts-and-minds[125] effort.

Desai was trying to improve her search results when she heard a heated conversation start up—physically nearby, not within the virtual space of her headphones. She blanked her HMD for a second and looked around.

The major was on the phone. "No, our troops have not fired on anyone! What you're seeing is a false feed. No, a false feed. I can see the market right now, everything's fine. You need to . . ." Desai turned her display back on, and was instantly high above Zefra again.

She felt a growing sense of unease. First the flash mobs, and now an apparently sophisticated real-time moblog aggregator spoof . . . There was

---

[123.] http://sigchi.org/chi96/proceedings/workshop/Friedman/bf1txt.htm

[124.] http://www.edge.org/3rd_culture/rheingold/rheingold_print.html

[125.] http://empirenotes.org/abuhanifa.html

more going on here than an isolated attack, or even an attempt by some locals to gain control of the city. It was all being played to a wider audience. The real purpose of the day's chaos had yet to be revealed.

∻

The strikebots hopped over the rooftops of Zefra, a formation of black canisters that bobbed eerily, as though weightless. Their fans were just strong enough to keep them in the air and they moved by kicking with long spindly legs that dangled underneath them. With their legs and dangling weapon- and sensor-arms, they seemed like armoured jellyfish to Campbell as he watched them spiral into the street. There were five of them; they dropped to balance in front of the damaged Camel, fans humming.

"Lord save us," muttered Daz. "It's the Martians."

"I know you don't like them," said Campbell. "Would you rather go through that doorway?"

"I never said anything."

Campbell called up the bots' menu in his HMD. A big power-level bar appeared; he could almost see it dropping as the bots stood there, though. He uploaded the information from his own HMD to the bots, including the identified enemy and civilians and the scans of the sniper's building. The strikebots ran twenty-five simulations[126] of an assault on the building in the time it took him to speak the command to set them loose.

"Supremely creepy," said Daz as they watched the bots go to work. With their fans barely keeping them upright, they appeared to stagger forward as if out of control. But they moved quickly and bounced over any obstacles in the way. One of the bots shoved an arm into the doorjamb of the front door and fired off a small explosive charge. There was a sharp bang and the door swung outward, knocking the bot spinning into the centre of the street. While it recovered the others swarmed through the door.

Something happened to the first bot, a booby-trap maybe; Campbell watched its feed go dead. Then nothing, as the others moved in. A new window to a camera view from the new leader bot automatically opened on his HMD. The image, although digitally stabilized, ducked and bounced crazily but was clear enough to show that the stairs were empty.

The swarmbots had infiltrated the lower part of the building. Their Doppler

---

[126.] http://cgw.pennnet.com/Articles/Article_Display.cfm?Section=Archives&
Subsection=Display&ARTICLE_ID=49998&KEYWORD=simulation%20military

JIMP (joint, inter-agency, multinational, public) capabilities will feed directly into future operations. A strategic analyst assists front-line troops in Zefra.

radar scans still showed three people in the stairwell.

The strikebot's camera, on the other hand, showed only three coffee-can sized canisters with pulsing balloons on top, neatly lined up on the steps. Campbell swore. "They spoofed us!"

The balloons were made of a rubber compound that looked like muscle tissue to the radar; they pulsated at the same rate as a human heartbeat. To the swarmbots, they registered as people.

The strikebots bounded on up the stairs and the swarmbots followed. According to the swarmbots' radar, the building was now empty. The strikebots quickly made it to the third floor. This was where the sniper fire had originated.

"They could still be in there," said Daz. "If they can spoof the radar, maybe they can block it too." So the three enemy who had been in the stairwell might be lurking anywhere in the building.

The strikebots pried open the door at the top of the stairs. A drifting bluish haze filled the corridor there. The bots did their headlong rush down the hall and through an archway into a suite of nearly-empty rooms. Here, tables, chairs and cardboard boxes lay strewn about as though thrown by angry looters. The door to the sniper's room had been burst off its hinges by the thermobarics. The door now ramped over an unmoving human form, and another body lay nearby.

Three prone figures lay on the glass- and grit-strewn floor under the shattered window. The haze had dissipated here; it was likely the sniper could have found enough air to breathe if he'd simply stood up and put his head out the window. That, though, would have made him a perfect target. Knowing this, he'd tried to get out of the room when the thermobarics went off over his head. The de-oxygenating bursts had outpaced him, however. He lay across the threshold of the room. The swarmbots now hopping into the corridor detected no heartbeat from him.

But, "this one's alive!" said Tam, who was watching through her own HMD as Marchand surveyed the street. She'd lifted the door and discovered that the person underneath was breathing.

"He's just a kid," said Tam as a strikebot nudged the small form.

Campbell ordered the bots to stand down. He tuned down the images in his HMD and turned to his team. "People grow up fast here. Take care of him, Tam."

"Things are looking up," he added. "At least now we have somebody to talk to."

Raymond and Ebun stared at the contradictory newsblogs. The commercial news networks, who mostly just poached off the moblog aggregators, were running stories about the aid centre bombing, with confused patter about reported gun battles taking place in the surrounding streets. Depending on whether you tuned into European, American, Middle Eastern or African networks, you got wildly differing accounts[127] that ranged from attacks on civilians by coalition forces, to the local government's line that nothing at all was happening.

"This is especially worrying," said Raymond, nodding towards a video feed that showed Canadian troops machine-gunning a crowd of protestors.

Ebun frowned at the carnage. "They're clearly using a game engine to invent this scene[128]. My friend's son has one, *Fire in the Gulf*, it could do this. It *looks* real, but will it stand up to analysis?"

Raymond shook his head. "The point is, it doesn't seem to matter any more whether the news is real or faked. Even when people *know* it's faked . . . all they care about is how it makes them feel."

"So what can you do?"

Raymond shook his head. "I don't know. If we hadn't had our information operations[129] budget cut to finance all the new kit we could have people on screen now countering this stuff. I'm not sure even that would work, though. How do you counter propaganda with the truth when the truth is boring by comparison?"

Already diplomatic protests were being lodged by some of the self-styled water barons whose territories bordered on Zefra's hinterland. The former nations of the area had long since dissolved into what the UN euphemistically referred to as "unorganized territory"—but their lack of central government didn't mean these places lacked internet feeds[130] or, for

---

[127] http://www.umich.edu/~newsbias/

[128] http://www.havok.com/products/index.php

[129] http://www.csis-scrs.gc.ca/eng/opehttp://econ.worldbank.org/view.php?id=24461rat/io2_e.html

[130] http://econ.worldbank.org/view.php?id=24461

that matter, money.

One of the policy flacks called Raymond over and they joined an intense conference call with counterparts in the U.S. and Europe. At loose ends for the moment, Ebun sat down to watch the drama unfolding in the city of her birth.

Not long ago, she would have been happy never to hear the name Zefra again. Her memories of the baking streets and walled compounds weren't pleasant. She had seen famine, the thirst of the water wars and running battles over oil well concessions, all before she turned ten. The AIDS pandemic[131] had wiped out an entire generation—essentially the entire middle class—and the continental ecology was crashing in a mass extinction[132] like nothing seen since the death of the dinosaurs. African through and through, Ebun had never seen a lion, or an elephant; even the scorpions of Zefra were dying, nobody knew why. Zefra was a place without hope, with no future, but with literally millions of people knocking on its door for refuge from situations that were even worse.

No—not completely without hope, she had to admit. The European Union had finally okayed a new associate-member status and was offering it to key states in Africa. Morocco and Algeria, Mediterranean nations with historic ties to Europe, were likely to become the first to become associates, now that Turkey had shown that Islamic nations could cohabit with the ancient states of the Crusaders. Oil pipelines were being laid across the Sahara, for the first time carrying oil to the Middle East from the unexpectedly rich fields in West Africa.

The pipelines had brought work and a new strategic importance to sub-Saharan Africa. Things were changing there, for the first time in centuries. But Ebun privately thought it was all too little, too late for Zefra.

"Ebun Ishangi?" She looked up to find a uniformed military officer standing next to her. He extended his hand for her to shake. "Martin Hutchison. I was told you're our expert on the local dialects in Zefra."

"I suppose I am, though it's been years—"

"Good. We have a situation on the ground and we need an interpreter for it."

She allowed herself a faint smile as she followed him towards one of the

---

[131] http://www.rense.com/health/aids1.htm

[132] http://www.actionbioscience.org/newfrontiers/myers_knoll.html

enclosed, glass-walled conference rooms. "Your translation programs[133] can't deal with it?"

"It's too important to leave to machines," said Hutchison. "Anyway," he added reluctantly, "this particular dialect is defeating them."

They sat down and he transferred in a video feed. The image appeared to float a few inches[134] in front of the blank office wall, but the overhead lights were washing it out. "Could you make it darker?" asked Ebun. Hutchison nodded and waved at the ceiling. The lights dimmed.

Now Ebun could see the image a bit better, but it wasn't very good quality to begin with: shaky, grainy and over-contrasted. Gradually she realized that the dark blob in the center of the square was the face of a young man, maybe even a boy. He was cursing in a mangled version of Bantu that Ebun hadn't heard in years.

Hearing it now brought back a wash of memories-few of them pleasant.

"What's he saying?" asked Hutchison.

"You don't want to know." She shook her head.

"You know the language?"

"Oh yes. I know it." It was a slum dialect of Zefra, a creole of Bantu, French and English. The language translation programs would have been up to the linguistics of it, she thought, but the accent was so harsh that even the English words were all but unrecognizable.

"This feed is from Sergeant Campbell, he's the section leader for a patrol that's been pinned down in central Zefra," said Hutchison. "We'd like you to talk him through a conversation with this kid."

She eyed him. "An interrogation."

Hutchison shook his head. "A conversation. The facial recognition software in Campbell's HMD will be able to tell when he's lying[135]. We just need to understand what he's telling us."

Reluctantly, she nodded. Her reluctance wasn't so much from having to question the boy; if this was one of the people who'd bombed the aid station then lives might be at stake. It was hearing the accent of the slums

---

133. http://www.pcmag.com/article2/0,1759,1612230,00.asp

134. http://www.3dmirage.com/content/production_holographic.asp

135. http://www.eetimes.com/story/OEG20040116S0050

again that upset her.

It was all still there—the cardboard shacks, filth-ridden alleys, places of casual rape and murder. She hadn't made it go away by turning her back on it.

She took a deep breath. "Okay," she said. "Put them on."

❧

Major Monet put down the telephone and grimaced at nothing in particular. Things were getting interesting. He had a patrol isolated in the center of the city, another two tied up at the aid station, and the continued presence of the flash mobs cutting them all off from reinforcements. And now it seemed the warlords of the anarchy that had once been Chad were getting involved. A fleet of Toyota trucks with machine guns mounted in the back was conducting manoeuvres near the border, and the warlords were making bold threats on the internet, claiming that a dire fate was in store for the coalition in Zefra. Nobody doubted that they had their eyes on the oil pipelines west of the city. But these were well guarded, and the warlords simply could not take the pipelines without support from within the city itself.

As he was contemplating this, a new message popped up on the board. One of the sniffer bots he'd sent to barnstorm the canyon-like streets of the city had turned up an explosives trace. "Desai? Bring up that location."

"On it, sir." In moments he was looking at a vertiginous shot straight down on Zefra's streets. Centered in the grey cross-hatch of pavement and dirt was a corner where a solitary car was parked. "It's outside the Red Crescent compound," said Desai.

"How long has it been there? Rewind[136] our view of that."

There was a pause. Then Desai said apologetically, "it's been there at least two days. The buffer doesn't hold anything further back."

How long had they been planning this? "We need to clear the area," he said. "Call in the EOD and tell the Crescent people. But before anybody moves on the ground we need to scramble all radio signals[137] near that site."

This operation had obviously been planned for a long time, he mused. In all likelihood it was timed to upset the planned elections-or was it? None of

---

[136] http://video.google.com/video_about.html

[137] http://soundandcommunications.com/audio/apr_03.htm

the new voting stations had been targeted.

The city was on edge as it was; the coalition's hearts-and-minds campaign didn't seem to be working. The last thing they needed now was a wild-card scenario, but that was exactly what seemed to be developing here.

Time to find out what's happening, he decided. And time to call in all the resources he could muster.

☙

". . . You don't want to know what he just called you," said the cultural specialist. She sounded amused. Campbell glowered at the kid. He'd been asking questions for several minutes now, in French since the machine translators insisted that the boy lapsed into that language every now and again. But his questions were being met with either a stony silence or violent curses.

They were set up on the main floor of the building, in an office space with old wooden desks and large portraits of bearded glowering men on the walls. Daz stood over the boy, and Marchand was watching out the window. After plugging themselves in for a quick recharge[138], the strikebots were patrolling the streets outside. Nobody was coming anywhere near them.

"This is getting us nowhere," he muttered. "Unless I know what Plan B was, I'm not moving from this place." He really wanted to chase the remaining three attackers, but since reinforcements were still tied up by the flash mobs, that was looking less and less wise. Desai had told him that the people who'd run out the back doors of this building had mostly vanished inside other structures in the nearby streets. As people entered and emerged from apartments, shops and offices, the attackers had vanished—their signal drowned by noise.

"Sergeant?" The cultural specialist sounded contrite. "May I try? I mean, talk to him directly."

Campbell thought about it. It couldn't hurt. He thumbed on his smartsuit's speaker and said, "fine then. You're on."

The boy jolted in surprise as a woman's voice emerged from Campbell's lapel. He stared at Campbell for a moment, listening to the staccato torrent of words. Then he looked away and laughed under his breath.

---

[138] http://www.voyle.net/Nano Battery/Nano Battery 2005-0003.htm

"What did you just say?"

"Nothing," said Ebun Ishangi. Campbell somehow knew that whatever she'd said to the boy, it had been at his expense. He glared at the kid, who glanced up and quickly looked away.

Ebun spoke again, more slowly now. She was talking in the same mangled and strident creole the boy had been using. After a minute, the boy asked something, and she replied at length. An incredulous expression slowly spread across his face.

"What did you just tell him?"

"He asked where I was," said Ebun in English. "I told him I was in Ottawa, in Canada. I told him there was snow on the ground.

"My name is Ebun Ishangi," she said to the boy. "I'm from the slums but I got out. What's your name?"

"I don't believe you," the boy said sullenly. "Nobody gets out." He looked away for a moment, then added, "Ishangi. There's an Ishangi who ran the water distribution centre when the UN was here."

"My uncle. He's a bad man, he's one of the reasons I left."

A slow smile spread across the boy's face. "We call him the little dictator."

"We called him worse things."

"How could you have gotten out? I think you're lying, you're talking from the edge of town somewhere."

"No. Why is it so hard to imagine I'm on the other side of the world? You've seen internet links." The boy shrugged, and encouraged, Ebun said, "I'll tell you what. You tell me one thing, I'll tell you one."

"Are they going to shoot me?"

"The soldiers? No! They might even let you go. Tell me your name."

He frowned, glanced at the men with their guns again, and said, "Suah."

"That's a good name. It means 'a new beginning' doesn't it."

Suah's eyes widened. "It does?"

"So tell me, Suah, why were you with these men?"

"They promised to get me out of here[139]. To . . . send me to a school in the east. They were not my friends. But they said there was no other way to escape the slums."

"But that's not true. I got out."

"How!"

"I'll tell you, but first you have to tell me where the men who attacked this patrol went."

"No. You tell me first. How did you escape?"

In the little conference room, half way round the world, Ebun smiled. "I got a job as a cyber monster.[140]"

A few minutes later, as Campbell's hamstrings were starting to ache from squatting in front of the boy, Ebun suddenly switched to English and said, "they're headed for the industrial sector. The water treatment plant."

"Ops, did you copy that?"

"Affirmative. Patrol, reinforcements are about two minutes away. You're to join them and head immediately to the plant."

Campbell glowered at the boy. "Yes, sir, but may I point out the lie detectors go off every time this kid opens his mouth. He's an enemy combatant. Why would he tell us the truth?"

"It's called establishing rapport," said Ebun Ishangi. Campbell reluctantly admitted that the lie detector[141] hadn't flashed red to anything the boy had said in the past several minutes.

"You have your orders, Sergeant," the Ops O said.

"Yes, sir," he said. "Move out," he told his men. "We'll try to revive the Camel." The vehicle's sensor network[142] showed that it had a flat tire and some compromised armour, but was otherwise in driving condition.

"The child is asking whether you'll let him go," said Ebun as they descended the stairs.

139. http://www.ginie.org/ginie-crises-links/childsoldiers/human.html

140. http://news.bbc.co.uk/1/hi/technology/3135247.stm

141. http://news.bbc.co.uk/1/hi/health/4397269.stm

142. http://www.eng.auburn.edu/users/lim/sensit.html

"No! What just happened here? He's an enemy soldier who tried to kill us. He's probably lying about the plant."

"Actually, he's a starving kid who's desperately looking for a way out of his situation."

"Well, don't ask me to be sympathetic."

"Fair enough. But the analysts here had me ask the boy a particular set of questions and then your HMD relayed his responses. He doesn't show strong commitment to the ideas of the insurgence."

"Oh? Pardon me if I don't believe him quite so easily." He watched Daz and Marchand descend on the Camel, while strikebots danced around them like some game programmer's nightmare about fairy circles.

The boy abruptly said something, pointing up the street towards the distant, unseen towers of the city's core.

"He's asking whether you know anybody at the *Hinterworld* office uptown," said Ebun. "I already told him it wasn't my game, I was back in the days of *Sheer Power*."

"*Hinterworld?*" Campbell stared at the boy. "Isn't that an on-line game?"

"Massively multiplayer[143], yes," said Ebun. "And that's what this is all about, for Suah and his friends. *Hinterworld* is one of a number of game companies that subcontract[144] to places like this. Zefra's in the same time zone as most of Europe. So they hire people to play monsters in the games, for pennies a day."

Campbell had a sudden insight. "Was that how you got out of Zefra?"

"Yes," admitted Ebun. "I pretended to be something called a Cyborg Queen all day every day for six months. There were sixteen of us, with a high turnover. The others either quit in disgust, or ended up breaking character to ask for help from the players through the chat interface. I knew better—the last thing these people wanted was to find out that the dragon they were fighting was being controlled by, basically, a slave labourer in a third world country. So I learned the terminology of the Cyborg Queen and stayed in character. God! I still remember every word of it! *'Die, biologicals!'*"

"And you bought a ticket out?"

---

143. http://en.wikipedia.org/wiki/MMORPG

144. http://www.wired.com/news/digiwood/0,1412,64638,00.html

"I got to know a player who'd switched sides—he was working with the monsters, just for fun. He showed me how to access the UN University courses from inside the game. So whenever there were no players attacking, the Cyborg Queen studied English and history. And yes, eventually I did save enough money for a ticket to Tunis."

"You're saying this kid was only with these guys because he needed a job?"

"Yes, Sergeant Campbell, and that makes him different from the average insurgent soldier. Most of them are well educated[145] and come from relatively affluent backgrounds. Suah was a hired foot-courier[146], he has no loyalty to their cause."

"Or so the instruments say," said Campbell.

"My own memory of Zefra tells me the same, Sergeant. My point is that he's talking to me now because it's the first chance he's had to speak to somebody who's been able to improve their situation without joining a militia or gang. He sees an opportunity here, so he's got incentive to tell us the truth."

A grumble of engines echoed off the buildings, and moments later, several vehicles of the relief force turned the corner in a cloud of dust. Marchand and Daz looked up from changing a tire, and then straightened up. Daz cursed. "They're just bots!"

Campbell looked more closely. The two trucks were cab-less, and behind them was a herd of squat multi-wheeled platforms piled with crates and equipment. These low-slung, cab-less vehicles were aptly named scarabs. Each one was surmounted by a strikebot in sentry mode.

"Ops, where are our reinforcements?"

"They should be arriving now," said Desai in his ear. "Only the bots and automated vehicles got through, sorry patrol."

"Well, how does that make sense?"

"I've seen this kind of thing before. People are willing to block a tank with their own bodies if they know a human being is driving it. But they're not willing to do the same to an unpiloted vehicle. Our boys are still back at the market, they haven't been given permission to use non-lethal[147] crowd-

---

145. http://chronicle.com/free/v49/i39/39b01001.htm

146. http://www.ginie.org/ginie-crises-links/childsoldiers/index.html

147. http://www.newscientist.com/article.ns?id=dn7077

Network enabled operations provide one option for improved communications in the future. A soldier in Zefra can access collaborative networks across the Canadian Forces.

control measures to disperse the mobs. It's a political problem."

Campbell shook his head, but he now had an uncomfortable feeling that all the eyes of the coalition were now fixed on him. "Get that Camel operational," was all he said.

∻

Mastan Nouria and Idris Kabadi had found their progress blocked by one of their own flash mobs. Rather than comment on the irony of it, Kabadi stepped out onto the running board of the truck to see if he could locate a path through. Below him, Nouria was chewing a nail nervously.

A kilometre behind them, Kabadi could see a flock of UAVs circling the white tower they had so recently left. The British had snuck around their roadblocks and were at the compound now. The streets were clear between them and the place where Kabadi and Nouria found themselves. Any second now he expected to see a pall of dust start to rise behind the obscuring buildings as the British decided to come after them.

"How did they find us?" he wondered aloud. Satellites, maybe. Or maybe . .

He leaned back, shading his eyes as he stared at the zenith. Yes, there it was: the thing the moblogs called an aerostat. It was a big helium balloon, though from here it was a barely-visible white dot. It was supposed to be just a communications relay, but he knew better. It was bristling with cameras and telescopes, and one of those might well be trained on him now.

"There!" Nouria stepped out of the cab. "It's Group Three!"

Kabadi looked where Nouria was pointing, but he couldn't pick out faces in the crowd, which was chanting "water, water, water," as an ambulance from the aid station bombing slowly crawled through it.

"And there is our way out of here," said Nouria triumphantly. Kabadi felt sick to his stomach as he realized what Nouria meant. Meanwhile his leader was waving at someone frantically.

Kabadi glanced back at the tiny white dot so far overhead. He had to admit, Nouria was ahead of him on this one. If they were being watched from on high, there was no solution other than blending into the crowd—preferably by disguising themselves as non-combatants[148]. Victims, even . . .

He wished he knew whether Achta had found the kids. But, as Nouria had

---

[148.] http://cns.miis.edu/pubs/week/031121.htm

pointed out numerous times, communication—even your own—was a tool of the enemy these days. Success at Zefra could be achieved only by executing a series of small, semi-autonomous plans in parallel. "We take our cue from the ant," Nouria had explained on one occasion. "People used to think that the queen issued all orders, and the workers carried them out. Now we know that the queen does nothing but breed. Each worker carries a tiny rulebook, with a simple rule for each situation he finds himself in throughout the day. The combination of all the workers obeying these simple rules leads to mass behaviour that looks like it is guided by an intelligent hand. An organization that operates this way cannot be attacked; only the individual members can be attacked. That will be our organizational principle[149]. It is how we will win. By being ants."

Now he spotted three more of Nouria's ants. They were converging on the ambulance, which had almost made it through the crowd. Kabadi felt light-headed and angry; he trailed behind Nouria as his leader strolled up to the ambulance and put a firm hand on its hood. The driver honked at him, but seconds later the doors on both sides of the vehicle were hauled open and men with guns dragged the driver and his guard out. Two more men were throwing open the back doors. Moments later they ejected two men who clumsily and with much cursing and pleading tried not to drop the three occupied stretchers that were slid—almost thrown—in their direction.

Kabadi made himself look away from the bloodied faces on the stretchers, and made himself not listen to the pleading of the men who were kneeling over them. He grasped the side of the big back door to the ambulance, and pulled himself in.

When he spotted a large white plastic case with a red crescent on it, though, he grabbed it and tipped it out onto the road. One of Group Three's thugs looked at him suspiciously. "It's taking up space," he said, seeing out of the corner of his eye that the men by the stretchers were scrambling to retrieve the case.

Nouria slammed the big doors triumphantly. "So far, so good!" he said. "Now get us out of here!"

It was like being a ghost, seeing an inevitable tragedy coming yet unable to touch or affect anything. Through the helmet camera of Sergeant Lesley Campbell, Ebun Ishangi watched familiar storefronts and compounds slide past the convoy. The flash mobs were all behind them—in fact, the streets

---

[149]. http://www.maml.hu/maml/model_summaries/

ahead were miraculously clear, though it was hard to see past the lead vehicle because of the dust it raised. Buzzing around that unmanned truck, swooping down and up with nervous irregularity, sniffer bots checked for any sign of explosives on the route ahead.

A constant low chatter filled Ebun's ears, like the murmur of the dead, inaudible to the blank-faced people the convoy passed. They were the voices of commentators and cynical political flacks, all talking on the newsfeeds about "this latest crisis" and the possibility that the fragile North African peace was going to collapse. The analysts eagerly anticipated a scenario where Zefra went over to the FIF, its hinterland following soon after. Like a cancer choking off blood to delicate organs, a blockage here would starve the whole organism.

Belatedly, the coalition was responding to the propaganda and disinformation. One newsfeed showed the rioting market where Canadian troops fired into the crowd; every few seconds the image would freeze and parts of it would be highlighted as an analyst pointed out that such and such a face repeated itself sixteen times through the crowd, or that the cracked plaster on a wall behind a bloodied protestor was identical down to the smallest blemish to "Wall Pattern 16A" from the computer game *Fire in the Gulf*.

As they drove Ebun read names of stores where as a young woman she had spent her first pay cheques from the gaming company. She watched the flat facades of others that she had never entered glide past as well—shops where she would never be welcome because of her sex, her ethnicity, accent or obvious poverty. Old resentments were remembered as men and women turned suspiciously toward her, then away (although of course it was Campbell they were seeing).

Suah sat quietly beside Corporal Tam, resigned now that he was sitting in the Camel with his wrists zipped behind him. She thought of mentioning the shops, of feeling out his own reactions to the streets of Zefra's small middle class, but what would that do, other than confirm that there was really nothing to save here?

And that was it, of course. Zefra wasn't worth saving. This sergeant and his patrol were running straight into danger alone and with no idea of who they might be helping. Would the city look any different tomorrow if the FIF won? Water would still be rationed; the AIDS patients would still be dying in the thousands . . .

They drove past a gaudily decorated disco. That hadn't been there before. After it were new houses, some without walls. And then a school. On its flagpole was a UN flag, and below that, optimistically, a swatch of EU indigo. She thought of the people she'd grown up with who refused to leave. "This is my home," one woman had told her the day she'd finally left for the train station. "How do you just leave your home?"

She hated Zefra. But she didn't hate her people.

Ebun swept away Lesley Campbell's camera view. In the dim little conference room, she appeared to be surrounded by hovering video screens—all projections from her glasses. On one screen, a commentator was talking about voice-recognition software. "There's a ninety-five percent likelihood that it's him," he was saying. Hanging over the commentator's own shoulder was a square image of a man's moustachioed face. Under that was a name: Mastan Nouria. "The coalition claims that minder calls originating from Zefra were made by Nouria. He is presumably there now, and is their top suspect in the aid station bombing."

Another window showed the aid station bomb site. "One extraordinary feature of this incident," a commentator was saying, "was the prompt response by emergency personnel. In fact, the majority of the people who responded weren't even on this continent. Flash mob response teams have been used for years; within seconds of the bombing, every person in Zefra known to have medical or first aid training had their minder ring. Many headed straight for the aid station. Remarkably, though, a quick-thinking aid station worker at the scene organized a handout of augmented reality[150] glasses. Through an experimental program started by Médecins sans Frontières, each set of glasses automatically called a volunteer medical worker in France or Morocco. Those that responded were immediately 'on the scene' through the telepresence[151] effect of the glasses, able to guide the hands of bystanders who wanted to help. Word is that triage was remarkably organized and swift and that several lives were saved through extraordinary interventions that could not otherwise have occurred."

There was a lot more going on—people talking, phone cams showing wavering street shots of the city, video being analyzed and maps showing little dotted lines of FIF and "unorganized" territories. It was bewildering, almost overwhelming, and for a few seconds, Ebun could see no pattern to it at all.

Then a sound of shouting—familiar voices—came to her. She heard automatic weapons fire. She cast about for the window she'd thrust aside a

---

[150.] http://www.newscientist.com/article.ns?id=dn6965&print=true

[151.] http://www.ercim.org/publication/Ercim_News/enw31/breiteneder.html

few minutes before and maximized it—

—Finding herself in the Camel with shouting Sergeant Campbell who was directing his men to return fire even as hammering impacts of bullets rang against the vehicle's shell. The sinister shadows of strikebots flitted past the windows and suddenly the glass of one cracked and there was blood in the air and on the dashboard.

Ebun cried out, raising her hands as if she could protect herself from the bullets, and then the video feed cut out.

DISCUSSION

Future Security Environment

"Ripples" introduces the reader to the intertwined nature of a 3-Block War where the transition from fighting to diplomacy and back again are often blurred.

The future security environment in these theatres promises to be a challenge to even the most robust doctrines and Rules of Engagement. Some issues to consider include the importance of Information Operations, a changing political scene, unorganized territory, and political disruption.

Consider the following questions:

1.   What will be some of the critical factors in conducting Information Operations in the future? How will emerging technologies shape the conduct of Information Operations?

2.   How will rapidly changing political scenes affect Canadian missions once already in theatre? What are some of the things to consider should the political situation change while troops are deployed on the ground?

3.   How should the Army deal with political disruption within its area of operations? What effect might it have on soldiers and what precautions may be taken to deal with it?

4.   We often hear the term "strategic corporal," as military activities by a single soldier on the ground can have lasting political effects. Should future soldiers also be trained as ambassadors and diplomats?

Emerging Technologies

The individual soldier will have increasingly potent tools and technologies at their disposal for the conduct of operations in a future 3-Block War type environment. In this section we see soldiers bringing tools from both inside and outside of theatre to bear on operations.

Emerging technologies may include information multi-tasking capabilities; real time planning and tasking relying on situational awareness fed into the database as situations develop; robots for entering hazardous locations ahead of troops; and increased bandwidth requirements and rationing for medical telepresence.

Consider the following questions:

1.   How will the application of robots or mini-bots affect tactics in the section attack in the future? What special considerations should made, if any?

2.   What might soldiers do to deal with electronic media and other means of instantaneous communications that may affect their immediate area of operations?

3.   The soldiers employ a translator half a world away to assist with their investigation. What other off-site resources might soldiers need or want to enhance their effectiveness in theatre?

4.   What sort or benefits and constraints will visual media have on Army operations in the future? What should be done to help soldiers prepare for this emerging technological trend?

Future Battlespace

The future battlespace will continue to be dynamic and in many ways unpredictable. In order to reduce the "fog of war" as much as possible, increased effort is being made to prepare for operations, reduce timings and increase situational awareness. Ensuring that the right tools are available right down to the tactical level to shape the immediate battlespace may be a requirement for the future.

In "Ripples" we see pre-attack simulations, Information Operations and deception and the application of force enhancements to reduce timings and gain the tactical advantage.

Consider the following questions:

1.   What are the advantages and disadvantages of pre-attack simulations, mission rehearsal and training?

2.   Can simulators effectively replace real-life training?

3.   How can soldiers shape the battle space employing tactical level Information Operations?

4.   What is the trade-off between updated weapons and equipment vs. Information Operations capabilities-what is the right balance?

Allied/Adversary Developments

In "Ripples" the reader sees that technologies often thought only to exist in western developed states in fact can often appear in theatres of operations.

The soldiers in the story quickly find themselves up against clever adversaries, employing whatever technological countermeasures they can.

Consider the following questions:

1.   What can soldiers do to counter the application of flash mobs as enemy force multipliers and political disrupters?

2.   In the story we see one way the adversary spoofs the soldier's swarm bots. What other techniques might be used to fool battlefield robotics?

3.   Consider the terrorist tactic of acting as non-combatants or employing semi-autonomous networks to counter army operations. How might soldiers counter these tactics?

4.   What other low-tech responses to high-tech force enhancement might one expect from the adversary?

The Human Dimension

In "Ripples" the soldiers feel the full weight of public scrutiny on their actions. From the application of robots as attackers to the reporting by the media, the human dimension is very much present in every aspect of their mission.

The soldiers must deal with the impact of current media sensationalism as well as the moral, ethical and legal implications of using autonomous robots to strike.

Consider the following questions:

1.   What are the implications of having robots attack humans? How will Rules of Engagement be affected by the addition of autonomous systems and what legal implications may be faced with the employment of strikebots?

2.   Where are the linkages between reporters and soldiers on the ground? Is a public affairs officer enough or will every soldier ultimately become a public affairs officer for the army?

3.   Can technology help soldiers understand intent better? Will technology help us identify non-combatant from adversary, and if so, how?

4.   What cultural tools do soldiers need for future missions?

PART 3
SHOCKWAVES

❧

". . . It came through an anonymous[152] remailer[153] sir," said Desai. "I can't trace the source that way. However, I might be able to correlate the signal to cell-phone use in the city. If this is live."

Monet shook his head. "It won't be. I'm sure it doesn't even originate within the city."

A low-resolution video image of Mastan Nouria was displayed on the main board. He was speaking; right now thousands of people on the streets of Zefra would be staring at the palms of their hands as his message murmured out of their minders.

Nouria's message was simple: kick out the foreigners. Zefra was an ancient city, he was saying, capable of solving its own problems. Right now its problems were the artificial solutions imposed by neo-colonials under the guise of the UN. It was standard FIF stuff and they'd heard it all before, but with thousands of people already in the streets because of the previous flash mobs, the population was unusually volatile and, possibly, receptive to any call to action.

Monet had just gotten out of a videoconference with Ottawa—again. As the day began there, African exiles were gathering in front of Parliament. The CBC had been called, a demonstration was expected. The Babel of opinions and propaganda that was news in the Internet age meant that worldwide, tempers were inflamed with righteous indignation over atrocities that hadn't even happened. To give credit to the Minister of Foreign Affairs, when asked on his way into his office what the government planned to do with its troops in Africa, he'd said, "you can have a quick decision or a good decision. Which do you want?"

But everybody knew which kind of decision would be called for.

While Desai took care of the immediate situation, Monet had been studying the flash mobs that had stalled their reinforcements in the city. The first two mobs had been created by simple bursts of disinformation: a bulletin on the Sunni forum of the network had told of soldiers raiding an historic mosque in the marketplace. All good Muslims were exhorted to defend the entrance to the mosque with their bodies or anything else they could find. This call to arms had come up simultaneously on thousands of minders across Zefra. It would only have taken a small percentage of recipients

---

[152.] http://tor.eff.org/

[153.] http://www.emailprivacy.info/remailers

believing the message for the flash mob to appear. As it was, the percentage was much higher.

The second message had told of a water tanker truck sneaking out on the old ring road. It was intended to snarl traffic ahead of the British force. This one hadn't worked for long because Zefra's few and proud drivers had long ago formed their own networks to relay traffic conditions—in fact, the networks had sprung up under a previous regime as a way of spreading information about new army roadblocks. It was kind of like the internet itself, Monet realized: roadblocks were perceived as damage to the network, and were routed around.

If only that were happening on the level of international news . . . or maybe it was, and the mechanism just hadn't kicked in yet.

The windows rattled suddenly; Monet heard the sharp sound of an explosion echoing from building to building. He stood up and went to look.

A puff of smoke hung in the air above the wall of the compound. It was just over the garage. Monet could see soldiers running back and forth across the asphalt. He heard shouting. Nobody seemed to have been hurt.

"I've registered an explosion, sir," Desai said. "I'm isolating the location." Monet turned, raising an eyebrow. Desai sat with her back to the window; her eyes covered by an opaque HMD and her ears cushioned by headphones.

"I've got it," said Desai. "It's . . . oh."

"That's all right, Warrant. I think the laser took it out." He eyed the innocuous pole surmounted by a dark glass sphere that rose out of the center of the courtyard. It was supposed to detect and hit incoming ordnance before any human was even aware of it. The soldiers cynically called it "the bug zapper[154]," but apparently it worked.

He turned back to the board. "I want the source isolated and surrounded in the next five minutes. They're keeping us off balance and I don't like it. It's time to bounce back."

Daz took over manual control of the Camel and brought it up behind the convoy's main truck. Campbell saw strikebots lifting into the air like locusts as, for the second time today, Daz and Tam rolled out of the door on the Camel's protected side. Campbell quickly turned when he realized

---

[154.] http://www.military.com/soldiertech/

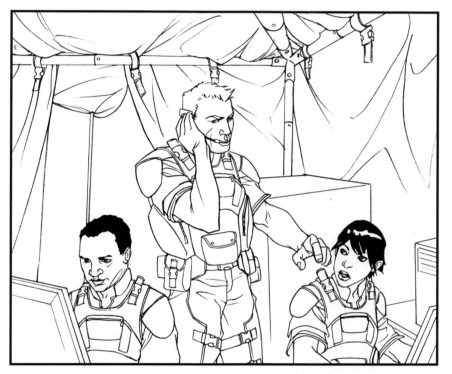

Future mission command. Bringing the operational functions to full spectrum operations in Zefra.

Marchand wasn't following them. There were drops of blood on the inside of the windshield. "Who's hurt?"

"I am," said Marchand. "We are." He was holding his arm, wincing in pain. Beside him Suah was looking down at his own chest in surprise. A red stain was spreading across his right side, just under the collar.

Marchand's diagnostic overlay showed that he wasn't bleeding badly—but Suah was. "Compress that," Campbell said, pointing to Suah's shoulder. Marchand winced, reluctantly removed his good hand from his bicep and pressed it against the boy's throat.

Talk became impossible as the air filled with the sound of gunfire. Surreal computer-generated lines and shapes blossomed all around Campbell, showing him[155] locations for strikebots, enemies, and directions of fire. Daz and Tam were hunkered down but so far they hadn't fired their own weapons.

In any case it was all over in seconds. The enemy were hiding behind an overturned car, but the strikebots were in autonomous mode now and took them out easily with a single grenade.

Campbell became aware of someone shouting in his ear as he rolled out of the vehicle and opened the back to help his men. "You all right?" It was Ebun Ishangi.

"Translator, get off this channel," he said. "Ops, we need a medical assessment here."

"Triage here," said a new voice. "I've instructed Corporal Marchand's smartsuit to dispense a 'shock cocktail' and a super-coagulant. Immobilize the injury. Move your head; I need to see the boy better. Uncover the wound. Rip the shirt off if you have to. He may have a punctured lung; check his back for an exit wound. Okay, I think I see frothing at the wound, you'll have to seal it."

Campbell's hands moved automatically through the procedure. He knew what to do, but having that extra voice in his head was immensely reassuring—and the medic on the other end wouldn't let him forget little details.

"Bastard didn't say anything about pain killers," muttered Marchand as Campbell was taping the boy's shoulder. He glanced over; Marchand shot back a quick smile.

[155.] http://www.sciam.com/article.cfm?articleID=0006378C-CDE1-1CC6-B4A8809EC588EEDF

"Your suit's supply is unlocked. Knock yourself out . . . On second thought, don't."

"I know what you meant." Marchand spoke the command that would release an anaesthetic through the smartsuit's embedded medication patch. "We better ask for a new car when we get back."

Campbell laid the boy across the seat on his left side and said, "watch him," to Marchand. Then he backed out of the Camel and went to join Daz, who was examining the burning car.

"Bots don't want to go," said Daz. "They think this is in the way." There was obviously enough room to get past the car; the bots were just being fussy.

Campbell looked past Daz. There had been three men behind the car. One appeared to still be alive.

"Call Command for an override," he said. "Then help me get that guy onto a scarab."

Daz stared at the unconscious insurgent but at first he didn't move to help Tam as she knelt next to him. "You're not thinking of sending the scarab back with this guy on it? What if he climbs off and runs away? I don't think we can spare a strikebot to escort him."

"You may be right. I'll check the e-map[156] to see what medical services are in the area."

With obvious reluctance, Daz bent to help Tam. "How's Marchie?" he asked.

"Fine," said Campbell. "But the kid's a bit iffy right now. We're going to need to get him out of here."

"Same deal about the scarabs, though."

Campbell shrugged. "Looks like there is a medical aid station just a couple of blocks from here."

Daz nodded. "So we keep on to the water treatment plant?"

"Clearly that's where these guys don't want us to go. What does that tell you?"

"Heh." Daz peered up the street for a few seconds, then said, "sure, but let's say we hang back a bit this time. Give the bots a block or so's head start."

[156.] http://developers.sun.com/techtopics/mobility/apis/articles/location/

"Good idea—half the bots, though."

"Whatever."

It turned out that the direct route to the medical centre several blocks away was blocked with debris. Since they had access to Desai's e-map database, however, the scarabs determined alternative routes, and Daz and Tam unloaded the two badly injured men while a medic looked at Marchand. His suit's left arm had stiffened into a sling[157] but he insisted that he would still be the best person to monitor the bots. Campbell didn't like the idea of taking an injured man into a potential battle, but he didn't like the idea of leaving him behind either—not if the city was on the verge of chaos. He trusted the people in the medical centre; he didn't trust the gangs of sullen young men who were hanging around outside watching him. So Marchand was with them when they re-entered the battered Camel and again clattered off into the dust.

They soon left the brick-and-wooden structures of the city's core behind, thankfully without encountering additional attacks—perhaps owing to the bot screen ahead of them. Spreading out to the horizon was a horrific barrio, the home for countless refugees. Some were here because of AIDS; some because of the ethnic cleansing of the western Sudan thirty years before; some had been here for generations. They lived in shacks made out of scavenged pieces of cardboard and plywood, under the hoods of cars that they'd propped up on stilts; the richer or more ruthless were housed in UNESCO tents.

Campbell had been told that the slum had begun to shrink in recent years, with the arrival of the water stations and the Grameen Bank[158]. One road bisected it: incongruously clear blacktop walled by tall barbed-wire fences that Zefra's local militia patrolled. As the convoy sped down that road the slum hovered to the left and right, just out of reach, like the parted Red Sea threatening to collapse inward at any moment.

Halfway down the road the lead vehicles came to a sudden halt. Campbell couldn't see what the problem was through the Camel's starred windshield. "Marchie? Tam? What's going on?"

"Bots see a checkpoint," came Marchand's voice from the back seat. "Looks like the local constabulary."

The Camel pulled up behind a scarab and Campbell opened the window to

---

[157.] http://web.mit.edu/isn/research/team02/index.html

[158.] http://www.grameen-info.org/

watch as some teenagers in green fatigues[159] and carrying antique AK-47s sidled up nervously between the scarabs and fencing. There were more blocking the path of the lead vehicle.

One grinning kid with widely dilated pupils strode up to the Camel and demanded something in the local creole. "Ops, we need translation," said Campbell.

"I'm here," said Ebun Ishangi immediately. He wondered if she had been monitoring their progress all along. "He says the government hasn't given you permission to enter the industrial area."

"You're going to have to interpret for me," said Campbell. "Tell him"

"I don't think so," she said.

"What?" He couldn't hide his irritation. This was no time for complications.

"He won't talk to a woman, and your helmet status indicates that you do not have the digital voice-over activated."

"Right."

More young men were slowly approaching, their walks insolent, their weapons held at the ready.

"OK, I'll drop it a couple of octaves—Ishangi, you're on," said Campbell as one of the strikebots that had been sitting dormant on the back of the next scarab suddenly shook itself. The youths standing next to the scarab shouted and backed against the fence, their weapons raised.

The translator's amplified "male" voice emerged from the bot. She spoke at length and the boy soldiers listened, including the leader whose weapon was now aimed directly at Campbell. After she stopped talking he stalked arrogantly over to the strikebot, waving one hand and shouting.

"He says he was ordered to hold this position. The authorities don't want to make the situation any worse."

"That's just great. I—" A low rumble like distant thunder rolled across the barrio. The child soldiers turned to look, and Campbell stuck his head out of the Camel to watch as a tiny mushroom cloud lofted up over the industrial section.

"Speak of the devil," he muttered.

[159.] http://www.ginie.org/ginie-crises-links/childsoldiers/recruitment.html

꙳

"Sir, it's my fault," said Desai. "I wasn't watching closely enough."

Monet shook his head. He was pacing up and down in front of the big board. "You can't be everywhere at once. We needed more eyes on the ground. That was my mistake." It was a mistake he was going to rectify immediately, he thought, by getting more analysts on-line to watch Zefra's streets through the aerostat cameras.

On the big board was a top-down image of the city's only water treatment plant. Tiny figures were scuttling across the tarmac, making for the main building. A fuel depot near the outer fence was on fire.

Apparently, this attack had been going on for several minutes now. As with all the buildings and streets in the industrial sector, the water treatment plant was dotted with smart dust sensors. They were supposed to be able to tell if anything bigger than a dog wandered into the area. Right at the moment they were obstinately reporting all clear, even as insurgents with guns ran right over them.

"It's some kind of worm[160] tailored to sensor nets," said Desai. "The problem is that smart dust components use a virus-like method for propagating upgrades to all their nodes. You can piggy-back a malware package on that, if you have some good tech wizards."

"You're telling me the FIF knows how?"

Desai shrugged. "They have access to the same websites as anybody else. All it really takes is knowledge that it can be done. Everything else is just innovative hacking[161]."

"Well, see if you can reverse it. I want to know what's happening in there—beyond the obvious." He gestured at the big board as he walked to the door. "I'm overdue for my conference call. Meanwhile conduct affairs as you see fit."

"Yes, sir."

꙳

"So that's where you've got to," said Raymond. He was standing in the suddenly opened door to the little conference room.

[160.] http://www.techweb.com/wire/security/56900090

[161.] http://www.newsfactor.com/story.xhtml?story_id=36129

Ebun waved a hand to shush him. "It seems that the explosion you heard changes things," she said to Campbell. "Now they want to come along."

"Tell them they'll have to ride the scarabs."

"They *want* to ride the scarabs."

"They're calling for you," said Raymond in a stage whisper. "Big conference call, sitrep stuff, Brussels, New York, the whole shebang. They want somebody with intimate knowledge of Zefra. That'd be you."

"I'll be there as soon as I can," she said, suddenly feeling anxious. Juggling drugged-out boy soldiers and heads of state at the same time was not what she'd expected to be doing when Raymond had rousted her from bed last night. When Raymond didn't move from the doorway, she snapped, "I can't walk away from this, lives could be at stake."

Chagrined, he backed out and shut the door quietly.

Her view from Campbell's helmet camera showed the young soldiers clambering on top of the low scarabs, laughing and joking with one another. They waved their guns about freely as they did so. She remembered that casually brutal machismo vividly. It didn't bode well if Campbell had to give these young men any direct orders.

But for the moment, talking was done. As soon as the convoy began moving again, Ebun got up and left the comfortable privacy[162] of the conference room. Outside, a subdued chaos presided over the open-concept office space. People stood in small knots, arguing or, all silent, staring at something through their HMDs. Raymond waved her over from the main pit, which was ringed with suits and uniforms[163]. Reluctantly, she came to sit next to him.

". . . It's definitely Nouria, but this isn't like his previous operations," an intelligence expert was saying. Over his head an image of Nouria floated like some sort of dark religious icon. "It's a carefully orchestrated escalation, and so far, we've been kept off balance. Luckily, we've simmed practically every eventuality and we think we know what he's going to do next."

"Which is?" asked a senior diplomat.

"Shut down communications with the outside world, if he can."

"How?"

---

[162] http://www.eff.org/Privacy/Surveillance/biometrics/

[163] http://www.forces.gc.ca/admpol/eng/defence/role_e.htm

"Probably an EM pulse[164] weapon. He can't take down the municipal power grid because it's a distributed system—he'd have to knock down all the windmills and substations. The power system reroutes itself automatically. But he can take down the minder network, and that's also the backbone for internet access. Unless you've got a satellite phone . . ."

"And a lot of people do," Raymond pointed out.

"Maybe, but the idea is to implant one message into enough people's heads, and then make it difficult or impossible for anybody to respond. Call it a propaganda bomb[165]. The message is likely to be something like 'the coalition has turned against you, but we're in control now.'"

"Ms. Ishangi, does that match your assessment of the situation?" Ebun snapped to attention as all eyes turned to her. "Are the people likely to listen to Nouria and the FIF?"

She stood up reluctantly. "Uh, well, first of all, there's no such thing as the people in Zefra. Zefra's a collection of cultures, not a single culture. The best Nouria could hope to do would be to mobilize certain key segments of the population."

"Do we stand a chance of identifying them—who they are and where they are?"

"You should already have that information," she said, turning to Raymond. He nodded and added, "since Nouria's sending his messages through the minder network, we can actually identify his recipients on an individual basis. We can even tell you where they are, except for the insurgents because they're using some other communications method we haven't detected yet."

"Can't we just monitor the network for encrypted text?"

He shook his head. "It's steganographic encryption[166], it's in the form of apparently innocuous pictures or pieces of music that have the data embedded in them. It's better to trace the messages back and isolate the ones that have come through an anonymous remailer. And we've done that, but the insurgents have all switched off their phones. They're running silent, to use an old submarine term."

"This is all beside the point," said the intelligence officer. "Which is that

---

[164.] http://www.globalsecurity.org/military/library/report/1996/apjemp.htm

[165.] http://www.btinternet.com/~rrnotes/psywarsoc/fleaf/gulfapp.htm

[166.] http://www.zen19725.zen.co.uk/oss/stes/intro.html

Nouria is making an appeal to local passions and at the same time doing a puffer-fish thing with his forces: making them look large and overpowering. If he knocks out telecommunications at the crucial moment, you can bet he'll have a low-tech alternative set up to coordinate his next move."

"Semaphore," said Ebun instantly. They all looked at her again.

"It's a gang thing, in the slums," she explained. "It started out as hand signals during silent raids, and evolved into this elaborate system that uses flags. All the slum kids learn it."

"Did you learn it?" She nodded. The Int O grinned. "This could be useful. Major Monet, have you noted that?"

"Yes, I have," said a weary-sounding voice over the HMDs. "We're going to need a crash course on this semaphore language. But at least now we know what we have to do to fight back.

"We have to hijack Mastan Nouria's message and substitute our own."

The meeting broke up with people splitting into working groups. Raymond was talking to somebody about game engines[167] and acquiring better photos of Nouria. For the moment Ebun was being ignored, so she took the opportunity to check in on Lesley Campbell's patrol.

They'd made it past the barrio, she saw. The high barbed-wire fences of the industrial area cast long shadows in the exhausted afternoon light. This part of town was theoretically secure, with checkpoints every hundred meters or so, curfews and bright lights at night. As they approached the first checkpoint, however, Ebun could see even with her limited camera view that it was empty. Campbell stopped the convoy and got out to check. Riding his helmet, Ebun found herself tensing as he entered shadow under the corrugated-iron roof of the shed that the guards used as shelter from the sun. She gasped when she saw the row of bodies neatly laid out on the ground there.

"Ops, we have civilian casualties here." The boy soldiers had leaped off their scarabs and started shouting angrily as they saw what had happened. Ebun seized on the distraction and listened to them intently, trying to anticipate what they were going to do.

"They're evenly split between the ones who blame the insurgents and the ones who blame you," she told Campbell. "A couple of them are saying that if you weren't here this would never have happened."

[167.] http://www.freeprogrammingresources.com/gamelib.html

"Which ones?" he asked. "Point them out, please." She did this on her display and it was immediately reflected in Campbell's HMD, and he said, "Ops acknowledge that, I'm changing the status of those three soldiers to indeterminate." She knew this had something to do with the virtual reality icons in Campbell's own heads-up display, but had never looked through a military HMD. She imagined the boy soldiers changing colour, from green to amber.

They drove on, more cautiously now. Ahead loomed the water treatment plant. It was offset from the road by wire fencing and a row of grotesquely rusted oil tanks. A good sixty feet of empty lot spread out around the plant itself, which was two stories high and largely windowless.

Ebun knew that Campbell was speaking to several people at Operations, but he was only letting her hear his side of the conversation. "Thanks, Ops, I see it," he'd say, or "we'll have to make do without them for now."

They pulled in behind a screen of sun-withered trees and everybody began piling out of the vehicles. Campbell activated the strikebots, an action that was relayed automatically to the operations situation display. They rose up in whirs of dust. One carried the now-battered box containing Marchand's swarmbots. With a light push from two of its legs, it hopped the fence and set off in a bounding run across the dirt lot. After a few seconds, Ebun heard shots.

Campbell turned to his squad. "We're going to gain informational control of the plant, then secure it," he said. "According to the simulations they've been running back at HQ, Fifi isn't interested in a hostage situation here, and their main objective is to control the plant itself. From a practical standpoint, that means controlling access, plus the backup generators, 'cause they know we'll cut main power from the windmill farms any second now. They might use hostages if they think they're under siege, but right now all they see is us and we don't look particularly dangerous."

Corporal Tam laughed cynically. "We're not, are we?"

"Not by ourselves, no." Campbell waved at the strikebots. "I know you hate these guys, Daz, but right now they're all we've got. Anyway, if I'm right they've probably imprisoned the workers with the exception of key people they need to operate it; we'll need to identify that location and take it. Us, I mean. The strikebots will head for the backup generator because nothing else works if we don't take that."

"Shouldn't it be the other way around?" Daz scratched at his stubble. "Protect the civvies with the bots and do the generator ourselves?"

"Why do you say that?"

"Well, Sarge, the reason I hate bots is because you can't play 'em. They don't have a morale[168] factor, and that's a big advantage to them. So say you're a terrorist and you're holding a bunch of hostages—and the good guys stage an assault on your position. If the troops coming in are human, you feel like, 'Hell, I'll hold up one of these here secretaries and threaten to shoot, that'll slow them down a bit.' But if it's bots coming through the doors and windows, what're you gonna do? You're gonna feel like Cleavon Little in *Blazing Saddles*, when he's threatened by that mob and he puts a gun to his own head and yells, 'nobody move or the black guy gets it!'"

Back in Ottawa, Ebun Ishangi raised an eyebrow. This must be some sort of movie reference, she decided. She wasn't sure whether to be amused or offended by it.

"I see your point," Campbell was saying. "If we go for the prisoners, they become an asset—as hostages. If the bots do it, the prisoners might seem to be just one more thing the insurgents have to protect, so they become a liability."

"I like my movie thing better than your banking thing, but yeah," said Daz.

"Standard tactics is to use humans whenever non-combatants are involved," said Campbell. As he said this he realized that the enemy seemed to know a lot about the coalition's "standard tactics." His gut instincts made him side with Daz's unconventional point of view. Once again, he was faced with making a decision that might cost him later.

Realizing that he was hesitating for all the wrong reasons, he cursed silently. Was he going to play it safe with his life and career, as he had in the past? Or was he going to do what he thought best for the people of this city?

Who's in command here? he asked himself.

"All right, Daz, I agree: the strikebots go for the hostages. Now, let's see what the swarmbots are picking up."

Desai could see it all. The city of Zefra was split in two, with the UN forces isolated on one side, only one patrol on the other. The insurgents were almost all on that side as well, though her crowd discrimination software had shown several groups of men moving to encircle the Canadian compound. These had started to appear an hour ago, and it had been a

---

168. http://robotics.vuse.vanderbilt.edu/Advanced Technology.htm

simple matter to send out several squads to engage them. All the insurgents were now pinned down in various buildings, nicely contained. Desai admired the cleanliness of that particular operation; it had happened so quickly and bloodlessly that it would probably never make the news.

The water treatment plant was another matter. As was the fact that the leaders of this particular cell of the FIF were apparently escaping the city unscathed, riding in several stolen vehicles including an ambulance taken from the aid station bombing. That would not play well at all, she mused, particularly if they got away. Apparently one of the warlords from the territory formerly known as Chad was ready to welcome Nouria and his men with open arms. And why not? They shared the common goal of redrawing Africa's borders along tribal lines.

Only a few kilometres outside Zefra, a flight of unmanned aircraft sent by one of those warlords was closing on the city. The coalition's own UAVs were in the air and on their way to intercept them, but had not yet received the order to engage. And somewhere southwest of here, a squadron of jets was taking off to act as backup.

"I see them," said Desai curtly. Monet looked over at the main board, where a new window had opened showing a speckly video feed from the aerostat. Way out at the horizon, a flight of UAVs was emerging from the unorganized territories. "Sir, they appear to be old Soviet target drones[169]. Maybe radio controlled, or refitted for autonomous flight." These were cousins to the toy planes her father had flown when she was a kid, though these ones had originally been built to tow target banners for shooting practice. They probably had wingspans of ten feet or more, and a small but significant cargo capacity. They could have anything on board[171]: poison gas, biologicals[170], or maybe just propaganda leaflets.

She forgot about all this momentarily, as data from the patrol's swarmbots began to flood in. The plant comprised one main building and several smaller ones, really just sheds covering catchment tanks and storage stacks. The main plant was a fiendishly power-intensive operation that probably sucked up as much electricity as the rest of Zefra combined. It had its own backup power generation facility, a building attached to the main one, with no doors on its outside walls. Built to contain gas generators, it had brick outer walls, a significant firewall on the inside, and blow-away panels in the

---

169. http://www.vectorsite.net/twuav05.html

170. http://web.mit.edu/be/news/synth_bio.htm

171. http://wired-vig.wired.com/news/medtech/0,1286,58104,00.html

roof in case of an explosion. It made a perfect keep for the plant's fortress.

But she could see inside it[172]. The swarmbots had rolled and scuttled their way into positions where they could deploy their Doppler radar and terahertz sensors. She registered a number of heartbeats inside the generator building, only a half dozen or so in the main plant beyond. The plant personnel must be hidden somewhere deeper inside, out of reach of her sensing gear. It was a maze of metal in there, after all, so the radar didn't work at all well. She'd have to find some way inside for the swarmbots—an air duct would be perfect.

Of course, the plant personnel might all be dead. That would also explain the lack of heartbeats.

After a minute or two of searching, combined with glances at her aerostat images of the plant, she spotted what she was looking for. "Campbell, I'm borrowing some of your swarm. I've found a vent that I'm going to use to send them inside."

"Good," he said. "What about positions?"

"Well, that's the bad news," she said. "The main plant has aluminium siding, as you can see. Very few windows. Fifi's ignored the windows; what I think they might have done is put a few rounds through the walls to make eyeholes and rifle ports. You can see for yourself on the bots' maps: there's men standing close to the walls at several points but those points don't correspond to windows. They're probably areas with heavy piping to hide behind, and some small piece of open wall they've pierced. It's going to be very hard to cover the ground between the fence and the main building with them in the way."

"We'll have to take them out, then," he said. He didn't sound too concerned. She wondered what he had in mind.

She was about to ask when something on the bots' maps caught her eye. "There's something else," she said. "Machinery moving inside the plant. Could be a forklift, or—"

"Bots?"

"I hope not. But these guys have surprised us before. I'll rewind the overhead view of the initial assault on the plant. They brought a couple of their trucks in then, who knows what they might have in the back—"

"Did you see that!?"

[172.] http://www.telepresence.com/telepresence-research/TELEROBOT/index.html

"What?" Confused, Desai shuffled the various windows floating in the virtual space around her. The bot maps didn't show anything unusual, but what was that on the overhead shot? A puff of white vapour on the roof of the plant.

"Ops," came Campbell's voice, "was that an explosion?"

"Missile launch! It went straight up. And there's another one, it's curving out over the city. Can't you see it?"

She looked again. There was the second contrail, a broadening pencil-stroke drawing out over the city. But the first one, no, all she could see was that circle of white on the roof—

The picture from the aerostat dissolved in static.

"Ops, what just? . . . Ops?"

Desai sat back and swore softly. The bastards had taken out the aerostat . . . . No, not the whole 'stat, but its cameras were blind. Communications should only be affected for a few seconds before things rerouted themselves. But unless the redundant systems kicked in, her eye in the sky was gone. That was bad timing, because she badly wanted to know where that second missile was going to—

—Blackness, and she was flying. Pain lashed at Desai and then everything was still.

Unmanned aircraft[173] did an intricate dance in the skies north of Zefra. The interlopers were little more than hobby craft, unintelligent by today's standards. They were smart enough to dive when they saw the UN birds coming, though; at an altitude measured in single digits, they wove around trees, power lines and buildings as they closed on their targets. The machines following were just as nimble, but they now had to contend with the presence of civilian targets in their lines of fire.

Worse, they hadn't been given permission to fire, and the link to Command had mysteriously gone down.

Swarmbot #34 had no such qualms. Its orders were clear: reconnoitre the ductwork inside the water treatment plant and set up a chain of relays if it found a way onto the shop floor. Just now it was braced in a vertical part of a corrugated steel shaft, air whispering past it and no signal to the outside

---

[173.] http://www.unmannedaircraft.com/

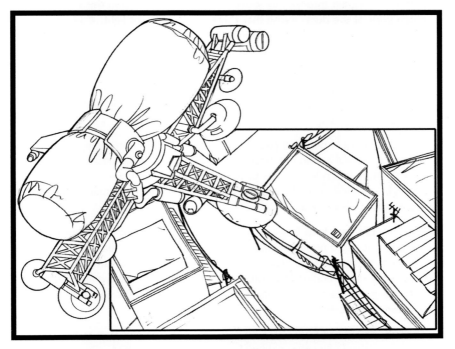

Aerostats provide 24/7 sense of Zefra City.

world save for the infrared flashes coming up from its companions below.

Swarmbot #12 had fallen down another vertical shaft and was out of touch. Number 44 was stuck in a narrowing of a side-way. These miniature tragedies weren't problems to the swarm[174] network, though; each incident was a valuable data point, enabling the whole to evolve an accurate map of the channels into the plant.

Using the gecko-pads[175] on its feet, #34 confidently climbed the vertical steel surface, finding itself after ten meters or so in a horizontal traverse pierced at regular intervals by louvered grills. Light striped the silvery patchwork of the duct. Now that there was significant light, #34 paused, snapping some shots of its surroundings and sending these down the shaft to the rest of the swarm. If Corporal Marchand gave the go-ahead, ten of the remaining fifty swarm members would scuttle up here after it.

For now it was in the vanguard. It tip-tapped over to the first grill and poked a fibre-optic eye out. The eye rotated, and back at the Camel Marchand said, "bingo."

Number 34 could only see straight down and ahead at an angle. That was enough to reveal a man in fatigues standing on a catwalk, near a vertical I-beam. He held a rifle and was peering through a small hole in the corrugated metal wall. The tiny shaft of incoming sunlight made dust motes around the rifle sparkle.

Swarmbots began leap-frogging past #34. Now that it had established a waypoint, it could no longer move. It would be up to other bots to find any exit from this maze. For now, #34 had a clear and important task. It bounced a range-finding laser off the head of the man below, and began calculating his exact position using its MEMS[176]–based internal inertial positioning system[177].

The other bots had found an exit: two adjacent sections of duct had split apart near the ceiling about thirty feet away from bot #34. One swarmbot locked itself in position at the gap, and the others began dropping through.

As each one fell, there was a loud bang! from somewhere on the plant floor, and the swarmbot's signal disappeared. After two of these, the rest of the

---

[174.] http://swis.epfl.ch/

[175.] http://www.sciencedaily.com/releases/2002/08/020828063412.htm

[176.] http://www.darpa.mil/MTO/MEMS/

[177.] http://content.honeywell.com/dses/products/sensors/satellite/mems.htm

bots wised up and stopped crowding around the gap. Clearly this wasn't a viable route.

Number 34's gang wasn't the only one reconnoitring the plant. Others had caught glimpses similar to its, and Doppler radar had confirmed the locations of twelve men at sniper positions around the outside walls of the building. They only awaited the positional information from #34.

The duct quivered as, far down its length, a hole appeared in its metal floor. Another appeared, and then a whole row of them stitched their way towards #34, accompanied by the sound of machine-gun fire from below. Marchand would later show off a short sequence of pictures that showed the approach of the bullets.

A tenth of a second before the final bullet punctured a hole directly beneath #34's six little feet, #34 completed its positional assessment and transmitted exact position information for the head of the man standing below. The information was accurate[178] down to half a centimetre.

And that was all that the circling strikebots needed. The men defending the plant had been watching nervously as the bots circled, moving in slow bounds like plastic bags caught in a breeze. The defenders didn't know it, but the bots were waiting as positional information accumulated. When they had it, they all opened fire at once and the corrugated steel walls sprouted dozens of new holes near the heads of the defenders.

"They're all down!" shouted Marchand. Instantly Campbell, Daz and the local boy soldiers dashed onto the empty lot that separated the fence from the main building. It had been a killing field seconds before. Now, though Campbell expected a bullet or explosion with every footfall, the way seemed secure. Buzzing low to the ground ahead of him, the sniffer bots were making another pass to check for mines.

In the air duct, swarmbot #34's camera showed a confused view of metal angles. Then the vent grill, which had popped and hung from a single screw, let go and fell. Number 34's antennae were still stuck through the grill so it followed, to bounce once on the concrete floor ten meters below.

Way up there at the duct, another swarmbot poked its IR sensor through a bullet hole and caught the data stream coming from #34—

—Which lay on its back less than a meter from the treads of something man-sized, metal, and armed.

[178.] http://www.ri.cmu.edu/pubs/pub_3600.html

As the treads crushed #34 its last image came up in Marchand's HMD and he yelled, "Down, down, down, down!"

The wall of the water treatment plant buckled outward as heavy machine gun fire erupted from inside.

୭

Idris Abadi's minder rang[179]. This was expected: the ambulance was full of ring-tones, mostly snatches of Koranic chants, which made for a momentary madhouse atmosphere. Most of the thugs of Group Three, crammed in here cheek-by-jowl, ignored the phones. They knew who was calling.

Idris checked his own display surreptitiously. To his surprise, it wasn't a broadcast message from Mastan Nouria, who even now was unrolling his own minder to listen to his own words.

Idris put the phone to his ear and leaned towards the ambulance's window. "Achta? What's wrong?" She knew what was happening, and wouldn't be on the line unless it concerned the kids. This was what Idris had been afraid of all along—that the escalating violence would reach the quiet middle-class enclave where he and most of the other insurgents had been living lives of deliberate anonymity.

"The kids are fine," she said before he could ask.

"Then why are you—?"

"Adanna's just packed her kids into the Isuzu. She wouldn't look me in the eye when I asked her why. Idris, isn't her husband the man who negotiated with the Chad warlords for that horrible weapon?"

Idris sat perfectly still for a moment. He eyed Mastan Nouria, who was absorbed in watching his own broadcast.

"Achta, get out of the city. I should have told you to do that before. But I'm telling you now. I don't care how you do it, but you have to leave now. Go by the old caravan route, don't take the new highway and whatever you do, don't go through the Colonial neighbourhood."

"But-"

"Now!" He clicked the phone shut and turned to Nouria. His leader's voice was coming from half a dozen opened minders. Idris caught the words, "If you have a sat-phone, place it in a metal container that you can close, then

---

[179.] http://washingtontimes.com/national/20050307-121323-4533r.htm

place this container on the ground somewhere well away from anything else metal. Do it now! In half an hour it will be safe to open the can."

"Everything's going like clockwork," Idris said casually. Nouria nodded.

"Hard to imagine that we'd need to use all our assets in this attack," Idris added.

Nouria shrugged. "The key to military victory is to use overwhelming force. Half-measures are invariably fatal. Look at that." He pointed to the sky, where faintly visible smoking streaks were falling. Those would be pieces of the aerostat coming down, Idris thought abstractly. Strange, he'd been anticipating this moment, but now it was here he didn't care.

"Were you going to tell me," Idris said through gritted teeth, "that you'd decided to use the Chadean weapon after all?"

Nouria shrugged. "It was a last-minute decision. All it does is reinforce the after-effects of today's uprising."

"Did you also forget that my wife and children are here? That they've only been here for six months?"

A horrified expression stole across Nouria's face. "Idris, no! I—I had forgotten. Please, you must call them and tell them to get out of the city."

Idris Abadi slumped back, staring at Nouria. It was sickening to realize that he didn't believe Nouria had forgotten. Nouria constantly talked about how family was a drain on resources, a luxury that a man fighting a war couldn't afford. Was this supposed oversight on his part intended to remove a distraction from his chief lieutenant's life? How had he intended to play this? Was he going to find a way to blame the deaths of Achta and the kids on the coalition?

Idris believed in the Fanonist cause. He believed that desperate people must use the leverage of global public opinion[180] and the shock value of the media to gain their ends. Hence, atrocities were sometimes justified. But he had to believe that the aim, in the end, was a sane one: a world in which wives and children could live the lives God had intended for them. There had to be someone who benefited, else what was all this about?

The weapon from Chad was too much. It wasn't even necessary, and it wouldn't change anything if it failed. Telling himself that, Idris leaned away from Nouria and opened his minder again. He would just have time for one quick text message before the hammer came down on Zefra's

---

[180.] http://ipsnews.net/interna.asp?idnews=22889

communications grid.

The message had better go to the right place.

࿊

Desai could hear, and she could feel pain. But she couldn't see anything. Either her hearing was damaged or it was eerily quiet in the compound. Rubble shifted somewhere with a grating sound, and somewhere else voices shouted. They suggested something to her, something she should be doing, but for the moment she couldn't think of what it was.

"Over here!" She thought she recognized the voice. Lampart, from Medical, that was it.

Sound of rubble being thrown around, gritty feeling of something sliding along her arm. So she had an arm. That was good, she thought.

Someone grabbed her shoulder, and Desai suddenly realized what she was supposed to be doing. "Over here!" she tried to shout, but it came out as a croak. Lances of pain shot through her as she was pulled up out of her cradle of broken concrete.

—And bright light flooded her vision. ". . . Take these off." Lampart stood over her in painful daylight, holding a battered and opaque HMD. Of course, it had been covering her eyes, that was why she couldn't see.

"Probably saved her eyes," another medic was saying as he prodded delicately at Desai's face. She felt pain there.

"Am I in . . ." she tried to say, 'one piece' but all that came out was, "pieces?"

"Lie down," said Lampart. Ah, a nice comfy stretcher, what a good idea. Desai slumped onto it and didn't complain when Lampart lifted her arm to give her some kind of injection.

The sky had seemed so bright. Now she saw that evening was coming on: there were amber streaks in the clouds overhead. They were pretty.

She closed her eyes.

࿊

Major Monet looked up from helping Desai onto the stretcher. Debris from the damaged aerostat was falling over the city, flaming bolts like Icarus falling from heaven. And far out on the horizon, four more contrails were rising into the air from the area of the water treatment plant.

The room that had held the big board now had a very big window. In fact, half the ceiling was missing as well. There was no fire or charring, as you'd expect from a Hollywood missile attack; Monet knew that such things only happened when flammables such as gasoline were involved. This missile had contained high explosives: it had simply punched the side of the building, and everything had fallen down.

At least four people were dead. Desai might be as well, if she had internal injuries. Her face was swelling up from the countless lacerations imparted by shards of window glass. The only reason Monet himself wasn't hurt was because he'd been in the other room, on his conference call with Ottawa.

"The lasers'll stop them," said one of the countermeasures officers. He was pointing to the distant contrails. "I think this one was just a lucky shot."

"Not at all," said Monet. He pointed to the rubble-strewn courtyard, where several neon-green tennis balls lay among the concrete chips. Several of the balls looked half-melted. "They used decoys. Somebody started lobbing tennis balls over the wall just before the missile arrived. Probably used a two-man slingshot from one of the nearby buildings." He shook his head in grudging admiration at the cleverness of it. "All right. Sweep the local rooftops, look for our decoy-throwers. Evacuate the grounds. I want complete dispersal. We'll use an ad-hoc network to recreate the command environment."

He shrugged. "Anyway, I doubt those missiles are intended for us."

"What do you mean?"

"I know what Nouria's trying to do, now." He gestured around at the wreckage. "This is just a distraction. He's after the city. We have to make sure he doesn't get it."

The officer frowned. "And how are we going to do that?"

"When I said dispersal," said Monet, "I didn't mean we should fan out as if we were under a mortar attack. We're going into Zefra, into every neighbourhood, wherever there's some chance to speak to the locals face to face."

"We?" asked the officer.

"All of us."

DISCUSSION

Future Security Environment

In "Shockwaves" the terrorist plan unfolds demonstrating a complex strategy employing a mix of human and technological tactics. The soldiers find themselves at the center of the action, and placed into situations where their decisions may decide the outcome of the whole situation.

Consider the following questions:

1.   What level of detail about mission goals should soldiers receive prior to daily deployments on patrols and other missions?

2.   How critical is such information in making what might become strategic decisions?

3.   What are the critical links a patrol must have to ensure successful maintenance of the mission aim when possibly isolated from their home base?

4.   What are some of the critical cultural and language skills that a soldier needs prior to deployment in isolated mission roles?

Emerging Technologies

Once committed to combat, a number of technologies rapidly enter the scenario in support of the patrol.

Consider the following questions:

1.   Do you think soldiers can depend on first aid via telepresence? What are some of the challenges that may be faced?

2.   What sort of immediate fire support do soldiers need? How might UAVs, swarmbots, and robot generated attacks improve or replace the current system of calling for fires or local manned air support?

3.   How might soldiers interact with local security to improve their own situation and draw on local resources to enhance their own capabilities?

4.   What types of technologies would you want to see/ have in terms of local fire support?

Future Battlespace

Timeliness, situation, and mission will possibly determine where decision-making and mission command is executed in future Army operations.

Consider the following questions:

1.   Do you think future mission command and control will take place increasingly at the patrol level or via oversight and guidance by a technologically enhanced Operations Headquarters?

2.   What are the advantages and disadvantages of having increased situational awareness at tactical headquarters?

3.   Will technological over-watch and supervision assist or hinder decision making on the ground?

4.   Who should command sensor swarms and local robotic support? Ops with its better overall picture of the whole area, or patrols directly based on their current situation? Why?

Allied/Adversary Developments

In "Shockwaves", we see further innovation by the adversary in the employment their own technologies as well as spoofing friendly systems.

Consider the following questions:

1.   What are some of the main concerns about adversary information operations? How might soldiers counter this capability in the midst of a rapidly developing situation?

2.   What sort of countermeasures or counter-countermeasures do soldiers need to ensure that their technological force enhancements avoid being spoofed from the adversary?

3.   What sort of shield and protection systems might soldiers need against adversary technologies when operating on foot?

4.   What sort of vehicle is best suited to aid soldiers in urban ops? Is it aerial, wheeled, tracked, walking, or robotic? Why?

The Human Dimension

"Shockwaves" demonstrates the emerging factors that will affect the human dimension of future combat.

Consider the following questions:

1.	What are the legal, ethical, and moral issues of employing autonomous robots with deadly force? What will be the impact on the Rules of Engagement?

2.	Discuss the importance of human intelligence gathering. Can the adversary exploit weaknesses in technology using cultural innovation?

3.	What are some of the liabilities of applying standard tactics, techniques, and procedures in an asymmetrical situation?

4.	How should soldiers prepare for environments where combatants, warlords, non-combatants and civilians all inhabit the same area?

PART 4
THE LOWEST CIRCLE

Campbell and Daz crouched behind a rusted gasoline tank halfway across the field surrounding the water plant. Evening was closing in and in the sky, strange things were going on: distant explosions high up, like subdued fireworks. Campbell's HMD was down, a red telltale blinking to indicate some sort of fault. And somewhere nearby, Campbell could hear the tearing sound of approaching jets.

"This is not an ideal position," said Daz. He was watching gasoline drain out of six bullet holes in the side of the tank. The enemy rounds had penetrated the tank but, since it was apparently full, there had been no air mixture to ignite it. As the gas poured out of the bullet holes, though, that was likely to change.

Rattling gunfire sounded all around them. Every now and then the weird bounding silhouette of a strikebot would superimpose itself over the violet and peach-streaked western skyline. Although he couldn't see her, Campbell knew that Tam was hunkered down a dozen or so meters closer to the building, so far unhurt as well, but unable to advance.

"I think it might be prudent to start back," Daz suggested. They had no idea what was happening; three of the boy soldiers were down, probably dead, and the rest were nowhere to be seen. Despite Campbell's shouted warning they had chosen to enthusiastically run at the enemy bots, firing wildly; this might have worked for them as a crowd control tactic in the slum, but it had proven to be a bad tactic when facing machines.

The worst of it was, he temporarily had no communications. He supposed it had something to do with those distant explosions in the sky. He thought about Daz's suggestion, gauging their vulnerability if they were to retreat now. Finally he shook his head. "We're probably safer standing here in a pool of gasoline. There's a breeze. It won't light."

Daz swore under his breath and at length. Just then, however, the gunfire that had become a monotonous din, trailed off in echoes. Simultaneously Marchand spoke in Campbell's ear: "—Hear me?"

"Marchie, we hear you. What's going on?"

"We've rerouted into infrared through the swarmbot net, Sarge. The EM bands are all full of noise; I think the insurgents are bombing the crap out of the city's communications grid. But our equipment is shielded."

"Great. I meant what's going on here, right now? Why's the firing stopped?"

"Oh. The strikebots put down the enemy bots, Sarge. They're inside the plant now. There's no more hostiles within line of sight of you."

Gingerly, Campbell straightened up and peered over the tank. Sure enough, his HMD's virtual overlay wavered back into being, showing a complete absence of red sightlines on the ground ahead. The water treatment plant's outside wall was riddled with holes, some large enough to drive a car through. A swirl of strikebots was passing into the plant through one of them.

"What about the roof?" He could see a drifting smudge of smoke up there.

"I took out the missile launcher myself with some grenades," said Marchand. "Great range on these rifles, let me tell you."

Campbell shook his head and grinned. He saw that Tam had heard this exchange and was cautiously moving forward. Far back by the fence lurked the young soldiers from the Zefra home guard. He waved at them as well, indicating that they should look to their fallen comrades. Then he and Daz jogged to the broken outer wall of the building.

The enemy strikebots had been an older model, obsolete in the West. They looked like big metal balls split down the middle; they rolled on their outer rims and weapons deployed from inside the split. The remains of three of them lay battered and bullet-ridden on the plant floor. Up ahead, the coalition strikebots were bounding towards the heavy fire doors that led to the plant's emergency generating station.

"Swarmbots have located the plant personnel," said Marchand. "They're alive, in a storeroom downstairs. Only two guards and they're in an outer room. They're shouting that they'll kill the hostages if we come any closer. We could wait them out . . . But they'd be easy pickings with a few thermobaric rounds."

"Best news I've heard all day," said Campbell. "No dead-man switches or booby traps? Good. Send in the bots fast before they can reinforce those guys."

Campbell's HMD provided a 3D overlay of the plant, provided courtesy of the swarmbots, which showed where the prisoners were. A stairway cut into the concrete floor led down to two storage rooms; one guard lay prone on the stairs, watching for approaching hostiles, while the other stood at the partially open door to the inner room. The prisoners were inside that inner doorway; all the guy at the door had to do was turn and spray the room with gunfire to kill most of them.

Future soldiers must still be trained and prepared to close with and destroy the enemy. Close combat in Zefra's urban environment.

The bots weren't exactly thinking this through. Each had sophisticated simulation software[181] derived from the sorts of online games Daz played; they were running scenarios, dozens per second, trying to find an optimum set of manoeuvres and attacks. From the optimum scenario, they would branch off more based on what might go wrong at crucial points. Like a chess program laboriously calculating every possible move and counter move, they were building a vast decision tree: if X, do Y. The whole process would take them less than a minute.

Meanwhile, Campbell stood looking at their potential route into the power plant. Towers of machinery stood between him and the fire doors where the insurgents had barricaded themselves. His own systems were running simulations similar to those of the strikebots, but looser, to accommodate human beings' tendency to go off-script when the going got crazy. He knew he was safe from sniper fire where he stood because the concrete floor was painted with virtual fans of red by his HMD, showing where the enemy's sight lines were. Pale green lines, also provided by the HMD, showed safe routes to cover near the doors.

Meanwhile the swarmbots had separated into two teams, one cautiously poking little fibre-optic eyes up at the hostage stairwell, and the other brazenly sweeping towards the fire doors in an open wave.

The strikebots signalled that they were ready. Campbell turned to Daz and Tam. "Let's run through the plan." While the strikebots stood watch, the three replaced the live view of the world around them with a virtual version of the plant. Then for a few minutes they were immersed in virtual combat[182], running, dodging and covering one another in the simulation, while their real bodies stood stock-still and the Zefra home guard stared at them suspiciously.

"Okay." Campbell tuned their displays so that the virtual plant was barely visible, a ghost hovering behind the real one. If anything moved in the place, it would show up like faint double vision, the real object suddenly separated from its LIDAR counterpart.

"Go!" Then they were running, across concrete and metal polished by countless footsteps, ducking and weaving in reality just as they had virtually. Ineffectual gunfire showed that the swarmbots' assessments had been accurate: nobody in the power plant could get them in his sights.

Meanwhile the strikebots went into action, whirling into the air like

---

181. http://www.a-i.com/

182. http://www.dciem.dnd.ca/publications/factsheets/a06_e.html

menacing insects. Campbell heard gunfire, and didn't need to turn his head as the leader bot's cold voice reported that shrapnel rounds had taken out the enemy at the inner door. "Low probability of hits on non-combatants," added the bot.

The man in the stairwell chose that moment to stand up, yelling, swinging his AK-47 wildly. He only got off a couple of shots before the strikebots had him down.

Then the bots were swarming down the stairs. Campbell heard faint shouts of panic, which quickly subsided as the bots identified themselves[183] as rescuers.

He and his team were now in position near the fire doors. The insurgents had punched holes in them and he could see rifle barrels poking out of at least two of those. But several swarmbots had scaled the doors and now clung right next to the holes.

The run-through had shown that the stairwell to the hostages was covered by at least two enemy sightlines. So, the first order of business was to disable those. Campbell ordered two of the swarmbots on the floor to self-destruct in smoke mode. With faint bangs both erupted in white clouds, which quickly towered several meters in height. The insurgents behind the door began firing wildly. Campbell gave a second command and the swarmbots clinging to the door reached out and wrapped their little metal legs around the protruding gun barrels—then exploded.

Other swarmbots had snaked their fibre-optics under and around the doors. Campbell could clearly see the insurgents posted at the doors jumping back, startled by the flash-bangs that had just gone off in their faces. They were only off-balance for a few seconds, but that was long enough for Campbell and his team to reach the doors. Daz stuck his barrel through one of the holes and started firing. He could see the enemy as red icons, as if the door were in some way transparent.

Daz was aiming at the enemy; Campbell and Tam, on the other hand, unloaded thermobarics, shrapnel and smoke rounds into the big cube-shaped room. As they were doing this a green signal in Campbell's display showed that the strikebots had safely evacuated the non-combatants from below. A glance back showed numerous icons being hustled away by bots and the green indicators of the Zefra home guard.

Except for two orange icons, which had separated from the others and were approaching through the smoke.

[183.] http://portal.acm.org/citation.cfm?id=861057

"Daz. Six o'clock!"

Daz whirled just as the two young soldiers emerged from the smoke and started firing at the Canadians. These were the youths Ebun Ishangi had identified earlier as making threatening comments about the patrol. Campbell had wondered where their real loyalties lay, so he'd switched their icons from the green of friendlies to an ambiguous orange. It was a good thing he had. He and his team hit the deck and as Daz rolled he fired back. Seconds later the two rogue soldiers were down.

As Campbell, Tam and Daz got to their feet, several strikebots arrived and took up position at the doors. Tam checked the downed Zefra home guard soldiers while Campbell and Daz hustled out of the way of an approaching flock of bots.

"What about these guys?" asked Daz, jerking a thumb at the fire doors.

"We've turned the tables and they're trapped," said Campbell. "We can pick them off one by one at this point and they know it. It's time to negotiate."

"Good enough."

"Squad, Ops is back on line," said Marchand suddenly. "And they're saying . . . fall back?"

"Say again? Patch me through to them, Marchie. What's this about falling back?"

"—Out of there!" He recognized Major Monet's voice.

"Say again, sir? We've secured the hostages at the water treatment plant, but we still have hostiles inside the power station. We need time to negotiate their surrender."

"Leave it to the bots, sergeant. You need to head south immediately, into the prevailing wind, do you understand? There's an airborne pathogen attack in progress on your part of the city. Get out of there!"

Campbell and Daz looked at each other. Then they ran outside. "Sir, what about the civilians?"

"They're locals, they'll be all right. But if you don't get to safety, you'll be killed."

"Sarge, we do have extra smartsuits aboard one of the scarabs—"

"This stuff may be able to dig through your suits."

"Oh. Oh." As Campbell watched a flight of tiny aircraft shoot over a distant row of trees, he realized what they were facing. "Come on, Daz, we've gotta go."

"But the civilians—"

"This stuff's probably tailored[184] to ignore them."

"How the hell—? What is it?"

Two of the little planes suddenly went down in orange balls of flame. They were being strafed by some small UAVs, Campbell saw, but for some reason the UAVs had only just started firing.

He heard jets again and turned in time to see something silver flash by low overhead. A thunderous explosion obliterated the distant line of trees.

"It's nanotech[185]!" he shouted as he grabbed Daz's shoulder, and ran for it.

"We were tipped off by somebody on the inside," said the intelligence specialist. "The intelligence this person supplied matched information we'd had about a shipment of interdiction nano[186] that was smuggled into the unorganized territories last year. That's what's on the drones."

Ebun stood, feeling discarded, in between the intelligence guy and a senior EU diplomat. She'd been explaining Zefra culture to the diplomat, who seemed genuinely interested, when the intelligence specialist had run up looking uneasy.

"Hang on, I've heard of nano[187], but interdiction nano[188]?" said the diplomat. "What's that?"

"Think of it as an artificial organism[189]," said the specialist. "It's actually built

---

184. http://web.mit.edu/synbio/www/

185. http://crnano.typepad.com/crnblog/2004/06/nanotech_arms_r.html

186. http://www.eet.com/news/latest/showArticle.jhtml;jsessionid=TPW0O0GIYWEHYQSNDBGCKHSCJUMEKJVN?articleID=22102744&_requestid=302869

187. http://web.mit.edu/isn/research/team07/project07_03.html

188. http://www.au.af.mil/au/2025/volume3/chap05/v3c5-1.htm

189. http://www.spacedaily.com/news/life-03d.html

out of DNA[190]—not DNA used to carry information, but DNA as a building material[191]. The DNA contains the mechanism of the nano[192]. Anyway, what we know is that two months ago, a FIF hacker stole some studies on bone mineralization from the Bethesda African database."

"Now you've completely lost me."

"The particular set of minerals in the water varies from place to place. You can trace someone's origin by analyzing their bones; we do it in archaeology all the time. The point is that this interdiction nano could be programmed to activate[193] inside a human body if it encounters a particular mineralogical combination in the bone tissue. Or it could be programmed to not activate, with the same condition."

"And that means . . ."

"Spread as a dust over a city like Zefra, this stuff could be programmed to kill everybody who hasn't been living in Zefra for more than a year or two . . . Because the minerals in their bones will be different. Or it could be programmed to kill everybody who has been living in Zefra during that time."

"This could wipe out the city?"

"Yes, but that scenario doesn't fit with FIF's ideology," said the intelligence officer. "They're Fanonists. They believe in an oppressive colonialism, one that's reinforced by media like language and technology. Think McLuhanites[194] hostile to the global village."

"So what are they trying to do? Drive out all the Westerners?"

"Yes. That's exactly what they're trying to do. And if those drones are carrying an interdiction weapon, they could do it by the end of the day."

"Well, shoot them down!"

"We're trying."

---

[190]. http://www.sciam.com/article.cfm?chanID=sa006&colID=30&articleID=0009D5CA-C218-10CF-BCE683414B7F0000

[191]. http://www.eetimes.com/showArticle.jhtml?articleID=21700333

[192]. http://www.eurekalert.org/pub_releases/2005-04/cu-nic040605.php

[193]. http://www.news-medical.net/?id=3067

[194]. http://www.codeword.ca/writing/sb_lrc_mcluhan.html

"I thought you had this Nouria cornered," muttered the diplomat.

"He's changed cars several times," said the intelligence officer. "And since we lost the aerostat's cameras we lost track of him in the shuffle. But it doesn't matter: he's using a fire-and-forget strategy. The drones are already in the air, and I doubt even he could stop them at this point."

The diplomat and the general continued wrangling. Ebun turned, left them to it, and went to find Raymond. "Could they really do that[195]? Kill anybody who's not a local?"

He shrugged. "You're talking about the nano? Theoretically they could. Programming a bug[196] like that one is a pretty iffy proposition. It could be safely tested though—just make a version that does something benign, say turns people blue. Let it loose in a Zefra market and see who changes colour. Then go home and switch the blue dye for a nerve toxin. The bug is bacteria-sized or smaller, it gets breathed in and permeates the body. Then it just waits for a signal to release the toxin. Any units that lock onto the right mineral cue—or it could be any other kind of cue, even genetic—release the signal chemical. And then it's a cascade effect and bam! the victim's dead like that." He snapped his fingers.

"It's one of those weapons that's miraculous or diabolical, depending on your perspective," he added wryly. "To the Fanonists, it would be a dream come true."

Ebun thought about her own childhood, and her attitudes towards foreigners in her city. They were just there, like anybody else. She hadn't hated them—but she'd known young men who did. Right now the foreign troops were a stabilizing influence, but with them gone, all the old animosities and criminal networks would spring back to life overnight. Zefra would fall back into old patterns of abuse and neglect.

Or would it? Those young men who hated the outsiders, many of them had believed that it was precisely the foreign influence that had kept the city from maturing into its own miniature state. With the minder network down, no internet, and nobody on the streets who hadn't lived in Zefra for years, who knew what might be possible?

She shook her head. It was a great dream, but you couldn't run before you could walk. Zefra needed the foreign troops to contain its many sources of

[195.] http://www.wired.com/news/medtech/0,1286,64292,00.html/wn_ascii

[196.] http://web.mit.edu/synbio/release/conference/synthbio.html

[197.] http://www.globalpolicy.org/wtc/analysis/0914sources.htm

violence[197], at least for now. And the city was changing. She had seen it herself this afternoon as she rode the camera view of Sergeant Lesley Campbell.

Still, a small voice in the back of her mind kept whispering, *that's what all the conquerors said. Did their promises ever come true*?

She wondered if the boy soldiers would laugh in surprise when Sergeant Campbell and his men suddenly fell down dead. The thought made her shudder. Better check on his progress, and stop wondering whether Mastan Nouria was right.

❧

Idris Abadi craned his neck out the window. Their small convoy of stolen vehicles was leaving the city limits. He turned back to Nouria. "But why are we leaving? The interdiction weapon won't harm us." *Not you and me, anyway*, he thought darkly.

"We're going to meet some friends," Nouria said past a tight smile. "The city can take care of itself for now. That's the idea."

"But . . ." He leaned out again to look back. Contrails glowed in the light of the setting sun. Somewhere back there, he had to believe Achta was on her way out of town. And invisible, perhaps even now settling around her shoulders and those of the kids, was a mantle of death. "Shouldn't we be there to coordinate? The revolution—"

"Is not our revolution, and is not for our benefit," said Nouria seriously. "We're not in Zefra to control it ourselves. Or did you believe we were? Did you harbour hidden desires for an empire, Idris?" He laughed at Abadi's expression. "Zefra is an example to the world of what's possible. It is its own place tonight, for the first time in hundreds of years. Look back at it! You won't be turned into a pillar of salt. You gaze upon a city that is cleansing itself of foreign oppression. All the devils of globalism are dying back there and what will be left will be its own place, pure, unpolluted by the language of conquerors."

He did look. And though he might not be turned to salt, what about Achta? Idris Abadi stretched a hand out into the wind, reaching back towards the star-like lights of the city.

I'm sorry.

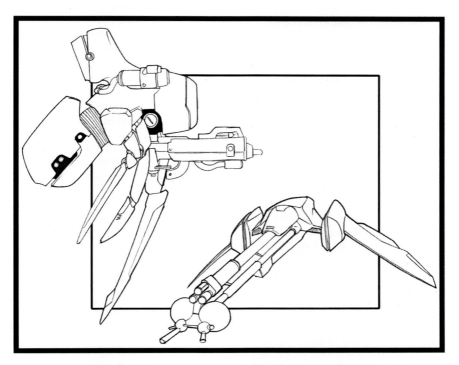

**The future of Act, Sense and Shield? Dragonflies, swarmbots
and strikebots supporting soldiers on the ground.**

☞

A small object, black in the deepening dusk, skipped over the distant trees. It wove back and forth with eerie intelligence, dodging lines of bullets that stitched the air around it. Behind it, two UAVs swooped like swallows harrying an owl.

It was coming straight for them.

"Bring it down!" shouted Tam. Before Campbell could stop them, she and Daz were running in opposite directions, their weapons on full automatic as they shot at the oncoming drone. "Cease fire!" Campbell yelled, but at that moment the drone passed in between the two soldiers and their crossfire hit it. It suddenly took a nosedive and without flame or smoke, pancaked on the ground. A cloud of dust shot up from the impact, and Daz cheered.

They were only fifty or so meters from the Camel. "Come on!" said Campbell. The two ran towards it, giving the rising cloud of dust as wide a berth as they could.

Suddenly Daz cursed and hopped a foot in the air; simultaneously Campbell's suit alarm went off. Red letters flashed in his lower visual field: Pathogen or Toxic Agent Detected.

"Patrol, this is Jacobs in Ops. Listen, don't go near that drone! It's letting out a cloud of dangerous nanotech. Your suits should protect you, but we don't know for how long. Ensure you follow all HAZMAT precautions as soon as possible."

"Oh, Jesus," said Daz as he hurried to pull up the flaps of his suit's hood. Campbell had done his the instant the alarm went.

"Let's get out of here now!" said Campbell. "We've got to clear the area. The stuff's going to be in the air."

Daz fumbled with the supposedly self-sealing hood. "And we're just leaving the damned plant to the FIF?"

"The bots will keep them penned in. I wouldn't worry too much about it." They made it back to the Camel and Campbell verified that Marchand and Tam were fully suited up before he and Daz piled into the back. "Marchie, get us out of here."

The industrial area faded behind them. In the gathering gloom, Campbell, Tam and Daz sat looking at one another through the rippling plastic that covered their HMDs. Finally Daz laughed. "I guess that's it for the day, then?"

Marchand chuckled, and finally Campbell joined in. Tam sat tensely, watching Daz.

She was the first to notice when Daz's laughing turned into choking. "Sarge!" Campbell turned to see Daz convulsing. He fell across Tam's lap, his whole body trembling. "Oh God," he said in a strangled voice.

"Ops!, we've got a situation here!"

The lights of Zefra approached in the dark, but help was miles away.

Overhead UAVs and older, manned jets curled in tight patterns, but their searching was useless. FIF was getting away with everything they'd done today. Idris Abadi turned from watching the jets and looked over at Mastan Nouria. He frowned. "You didn't tell me who these people are that we're going to meet."

"Our perimeter guard. Soldiers from the Chadean warlords."

Abadi stared at him. "But we discussed this . . . This too! They aren't to be trusted. They'll make Zefra into their own playground, and by the time they're done with it everyone will be dead."

Nouria smiled smugly. "Not after the nanotech weapon hits the streets," he said. "The Chadeans are foreigners to Zefra too. Like the British and the Canadians, they will be unable to walk its streets in safety. So we can employ them safely as guards around the outskirts of the city."

"And this decision was made by whom? Your precious, independent Zefra? Or is it Mastan Nouria who's playing the conqueror now?"

"Watch it, Idris," said Nouria. "It's not your place to question the plan."

Abadi sat back into the deep cushions of the Mercedes they'd stolen from a frightened Moroccan importer. Dark fields interspersed with the twisted silhouettes of trees flowed past. It was quiet in the car, and the sky was a deep azure with touches of turquoise that would have touched him deeply on any other day.

He pulled out his minder and quietly spoke Achta's name into it.

He waited, but no one picked up on the other end.

And if the nanotech weapon isn't successful? He didn't bother to say this aloud. Nouria wouldn't listen.

They were perhaps an hour from the vague border that separated Zefra's hinterland from the unorganized territories. Madmen with guns would be waiting there in the dark, ready to close some diabolical deal with Nouria. The coalition could crush these troops with ease, but Nouria's strikes against the coalition had all been psychological, in the end. If they had struck home, the foreign peacekeepers would be paralyzed when the warlords arrived. In that case, Zefra would fall.

But it was still possible to do something about it. He thought of Achta and the kids, and realized that whatever happened, he was separated from them now—either as an international fugitive, once the dust settled and names were put to faces, or as one more chess piece moved about by Nouria. More than the city of Zefra lay between them now.

He brought out his pistol. Nouria glanced at him incuriously, knowing that their guns were programmed[198] not to fire at any FIF member carrying the right RFID tag[199] in his pocket.

Abadi checked the magazine, ensured that the safety was off, and then rolled down the window.

"Idris, what are you doing?"

One of the coalition UAVs was rumbling by overhead, lightless but silhouetted against the final indigo of dusk. Abadi aimed in its general direction, and began squeezing the trigger.

Mastan Nouria wasn't able to wrestle the gun from his grip before the UAV turned in their direction.

&

Major Monet stood under the white towers. The moon was rising over Zefra; it was late, but everybody was up. People filled the streets, and they all seemed to be talking at once.

He sat on the hood of an armoured personnel carrier and watched his people work the crowd. They were handing out satellite phones, which he'd requisitioned from a coalition storehouse in Niger. More were on the way. The banners of e-paper that hung from walls and storefronts were blank now, victims of Mastan Nouria's electromagnetic weapons. But the

---

[198.] http://www.metalstorm.com/04_what_is_a_smart_gun.html

[199.] http://www.theregister.co.uk/2003/06/27/rfid_chips_are_here/

	LIVE FEEDS	
Free Sudanese Reporters' Guild	**BBC World News**	**National Coalition Council News**
"Well, we don't have the technology to tell when we're being deceived in such a way. And frankly, we had no reason not to believe the troops might fire on our people. Look at the incidents in '09 and..."	"As the moon rises a calm has settled over the city. Many people are out in the streets, some of them seemingly to protect the polling stations for tomorrow's vote. People are talking and even selling food in the streets. Tom a strange, almost holiday atmosphere seems to have taken hold here..."	"Rumours of insurgent activity have been proven false. The government regrets the unfortunate isolated terrorist attacks that took place today, but we have the situation well in control, and the vote will proceed tomorrow as planned."

city's people wouldn't be cut off from the outside world for very long. They weren't cut off at all, in fact. Even in the small areas where the insurgents' nanotech weapon had drifted, sat-phones and new e-paper were being made available. Nouria's attempt to isolate Zefra had failed.

An ambulance helicopter chuttered overhead, on its way to the industrial zone and Sergeant Lesley Campbell's patrol. It had already made one trip south carrying the injured from the command centre. There would be a couple more trips to make. But only a couple.

They had already visited the highway northeast of the city, where several stolen vehicles were still burning. DNA testing had already confirmed that Mastan Nouria was one of those killed when the convoy of FIF vehicles unexpectedly revealed its whereabouts by firing on a coalition UAV. The UAVs had made short work[200] of the escaping insurgents. It was a pointless suicide, Monet thought. But good news for the city.

In the morning, Zefra would go back to its normal business, minus a few people, who would be mourned. The aid centre bombing would not be forgotten. The combat itself had been so quick and so isolated that not

---

[200.] http://news.bbc.co.uk/2/hi/in_depth/2404425.stm

many of the city's inhabitants had really understood what was happening.

The coalition would not be returning to their compounds, though. Not for a while. Sitting here in the middle of the street, Monet understood something he hadn't before: that he was ringed by invisible circles of protection, ranging from gunshot detectors to explosives sniffers, facial recognition cameras aimed at the crowd, and lasers faster than any human and capable of shooting down incoming ordinance before he was even aware of them. Most of this equipment had sat idle inside the compound ever since it had been brought here. The coalition had used a very old strategy at Zefra, hiding behind their walls and sending patrols into the city. That wouldn't work anymore, not with people like Mastan Nouria around; and not as long as they had weapons capable of distorting the perceived facts on the street.

Nouria had almost denied the Canadian soldiers the city. Now that they were here, they weren't going to leave until they were no longer needed. They were citizens—temporary, perhaps, and barely tolerated in some quarters—but only as citizens would they win back the hearts and minds of the people.

An old man had wandered through the cordon of bots and sensors at the corners of the intersection. He bore no explosives and registered neutral for nanotech. Around his neck was a blank square of e-paper. Whatever message had shone out of that paper this morning, it was gone now.

He walked right up to Monet. Nobody stopped him, though the major knew that he was watched by any number of systems and artificial intelligences[201]. Probably, the machines recognized this man.

He grinned toothily at Monet and held up a reeking paper bag. "Curry?"

Monet raised an eyebrow. He realized he was hungry. "How much?"

"I sell on internet for ten bucks. My sign dead, my site dead. You give me twenty bucks."

Monet didn't hide his surprise. "That's outrageous. You could live like a king here on money like that."

The old man shrugged. "Not in Casablanca."

"What's in Casablanca?"

"Son. University. I pay, he go. You buy?"

[201.] http://www.cyc.com/cyc/cycrandd/overview

The curry smelled delightful, and he was hungry.

Trust had to start somewhere.

Monet bought the curry, for twenty dollars.

DISCUSSION

Future Security Environment

"The Lowest Circle" completes the story, and reveals more of the ideological reasons for the conflict.

Consider the following questions:

1.   Was Zefra a good representation of the types of Army missions that Canada may find itself on in the future? Why or why not?

2.   What are some of the most critical capabilities that the Army will need to face the challenges presented in the future security environment?

3.   What are some of the most likely threats the Army can expect to face twenty-five years from now?

4.   How will the future security environment shape future Army developments?

Emerging Technologies

At the end of the story the reader is introduced to new types of technological force enhancement and fire support.

Consider the following questions:

1.   Was Zefra a good representation of the types of emerging technologies that the Army will want and need on in the future? Why or why not?

2.   What are some of the most critical technologies that the Army will need to face the challenges presented in the future security environment?

3.   How will technology shape the Army twenty-five years from now?

4.   How should the Army prepare to face future WMD?

Future Battlespace

"The Lowest Circle" demonstrates a new way of doing operations using technology to provide safety.

Consider the following questions:

1.   Was Zefra a good representation of the future battlespace? Why or

why not?

2.   What are some of the most critical capabilities that the Army will need to shape the future battlespace?

3.   Will the battlespace be the same twenty-five years from now? Why or why not?

4.   How will the future battlespace shape future Army developments?

Allied/Adversary Developments

Real-time embedded mission rehearsal may become a part of future army operations as we continue to shrink action and reaction times during missions.

Consider the following questions:

1.   Was Zefra a good representation of future adversary technological capabilities? Why or why not?

2.   What are some of the most critical political, technological and cultural threats that the Army will face in the future security environment?

3.   What are some of the most influential technological developments you think the Army can expect to face twenty-five years from now?

4.   How will these developments shape future Army developments?

The Human Dimension

Interestingly, though many things change in warfare the human dimensions of war tend to remain largely the same.

Consider the following questions:

1.   Was Zefra a good representation of the human dimension of future warfare? Why or why not?

2.   What are some of the most critical factors that may influence the human dimension of warfare in the future security environment?

3.   Will humans continue to dominate armed conflict in the future or will conflict become increasingly autonomous or dependent on automated technologies?

4.   How will the human dimension shape future Army developments?

EPILOGUE:
THE NEW SHORE

৵

The tarmac wavered in the heat as Ebun Ishangi stepped out of the aircraft. One foot on a box, the other foot touching down on the soil of north-central Africa for the first time in years. A small step for man. Big step for Ebun Ishangi.

She blinked in the sunlight, feeling jet lag, nervousness and other emotions she couldn't even begin to name. The plane's sole flight attendant unloaded Ebun's bags from the pod under the plane, and she limped across the blistering runway to the city's new airport terminal, a sweeping acre of white tenting with loose partitions underneath. A few small knots of people stood here and there, talking. She heard laughter. It was quite a contrast to the tense days of her flight from her home, so many years ago.

"Ebun?" Somebody was waving to her underneath the dazzling white of the canopy. Several somebodies, as it turned out.

"The Major thought a few familiar faces to meet you would be good," said the tall young-looking man in the Canadian army uniform. "Warrant Officer Lesley Campbell."

She shook his hand, and both of them grinned. "And you'll remember a couple of members of my former patrol."

Daz Blackmore looked thinner than she remembered from the shifting images of Campbell's helmet camera, those many months ago. He limped a bit as he stepped up, and there was faint tremble to his hand as he shook hers. "Chained to a desk now, I'm afraid," he said in answer to her unasked question. "But downtown, where it's interesting."

Two other soldiers stepped forward, a man and a woman. "Master Corporals Marchand and Tam, yes?"

She shook their hands. Marchand waved towards the doors that opened out to the parking lot. "It's my patrol now," he said, "come and meet the new hires."

"Are you happy to be back?" Campbell asked as he picked up her luggage for her. Ebun laughed.

"No, that would be too strong a word," she said. "I could say that I'm happy to be finally facing my own past, and on my own terms. There's a lot I can do here for the people I grew up with, but I'm not about to settle. I've kept the lease on my apartment in Ottawa."

He nodded as if he understood completely. "So what does an industrial liaison do, anyway?"

"I'm not sure," she said with a shrug. "Helps with the micro-loans, I think. I suspect we'll be making it up as we go along."

She looked up as Campbell slammed the door on the dusty troop vehicle, and she saw the white towers wavering in the distance. A deep pang of emotion made her look down for a moment—an echo of old wounds, opportunities lost, and regrets.

Then she looked up. The towers were ancient, but they could be made new again. She would never forget the past, but she could make it unimportant. That was why she was here.

"So, Desai, what's our eye in the sky say about the traffic?" asked Marchand as he sat down in the Camel and he slammed the door.

A woman's voice issued from the Camel's dashboard: "The road to town is packed, as usual. But why should you care? You've got off-road vehicles. Why don't you just strike out across country?"

Campbell laughed. "We might just do that, Desai."

He slapped the dashboard. "Let's go."

જીજીજી

CONCLUSION

One of the aims of *Crisis in Zefra* was to provide an illustrated narrative of the emerging future security environment and those future army technologies as described in its sister publication, *Future Force*.

Another aim is to provide a starting point for informed consideration and debate of army future concepts and technological development. *Crisis in Zefra* represents but a single possible future for Canada's Army. What other possibilities may lay ahead for us? Will the Army of Tomorrow look like Sergeant Campbell's patrol section or might it be something completely different?

You can help us determine what the future Army might be through direct participation. Your comments, feedback and, most importantly, discussion on the subjects covered in this story are both welcomed and encouraged.

To leave a comment about *Crisis in Zefra*, or engage in the questions presented in the "Discussion" sections of each chapter, simply log on to the Directorate of Land Strategic Concepts website[202] and follow the instructions. Your involvement in this learning process is critical to the overall future development of the Army. Thank you for your interest and we look forward to hearing from you.

Log on at:

Crisis in Zefra Website

http://www.army.forces.gc.ca/zefra/

Visit us online at...
http://www.army.forces.gc.ca/zefra/

[202.] http://armyapp.forces.gc.ca/dlsc-dcsot/

ANNEX A—
Anatomy of a Failed State

ZEFRA:
PORTRAIT OF A FAILED STATE

Peter Gizewski

Zefra, within which this military scenario unfolds, is clearly a fictional construct. No such national entity exists. Much like the details presented for the military scenario itself, however, Zefra offers a glimpse of future possibilities—possibilities that could ultimately become real both in light of ongoing trends and an inability (or unwillingness) on the part of the international community to effectively manage (and hopefully contain) their potential impacts in the decades ahead.

In fact, Zefra represents a microcosm of destabilizing forces that are alive and well even within the current international security environment. These forces include: resource scarcities, highly corrupt and failing states, distributional inequities and identity issues (i.e. ethnic and quasi-religious hatreds), well-armed and highly-organized insurgent and terrorist groups contesting state power and legitimacy, and a world in which processes of globalization and technological change ensure increased access to key means of power—both military and political—both on the part of states themselves as well as non-state actors.

In Zefra's case, however, such forces are captured at their most destabilizing. Indeed, as they coalesce, they become mutually reinforcing; leading the small city-state into an ever-increasing spiral of human misery, anarchy and armed conflict.

The Road to Conflict

Emerging as an independent entity after a long and troubled history of colonial rule, Zefra exhibits conditions much like those of many states currently occupying the developing world (e.g. Sub-Saharan, Central and West Africa). With an ethnically diverse, sparsely educated, and rapidly growing population, a semi-modern (primarily agrarian) economy and highly dependent on foreign aid, the nation maintains an uneasy existence in the years following independence—all the while exceedingly vulnerable to the whims of external actors and unfavourable climatic conditions.

Consolidation proves very elusive—as an inexperienced leadership becomes exceedingly incapable of managing the demands posed by a young, rapidly expanding population tied to a limited resource base. As population growth strains finite resources, distributional disputes increasingly arise within the state's multi-ethnic populace. As well, disputes with regional rivals over access to fresh water work to heighten tensions even further. Meanwhile, declining economic conditions on the international front gradually reduce the prospects of relief from foreign aid to the point where large-scale famine is imminent.

Gradually, government legitimacy dwindles and challenger organizations arise to contest state power. Central among such forces is the *Fanonist Irredentist Fellaheen* (FIF)—a radical group seeking massive redistribution of national wealth and espousing a quasi-socialist, anti-western ideology. Under its leader, Mastan Nouria, the group develops a well-organized network throughout Zefrian society and increasingly engages in a steady and ever bolder stream of propagandistic attacks against the government—charging it with incompetence, corruption and the "selling out" of Zefra's future to foreign interests. Demonstrations organized by FIF leadership soon lead to rioting and looting. And cases of attacks against foreigners within the country increase. Government efforts to counter such actions prove increasingly heavy-handed, repressive and ultimately ineffective.

As economic and societal conditions further worsen, state revenues fall. So too, does the capacity of Zefra's official leadership to maintain order and stability.

Growing Instability

Soon, large parts of the city-state are left with little in the form of law and order. Vast areas become war zones—with FIF and government forces clashing in ever more bloody battles. As areas of the city become increasingly cut off from even the most basic of services, disease spreads. Meanwhile, fears of aggression from abroad increase—as state officials increasingly worry that Zefra's persistent instability could soon prompt territorial incursion if not annexation at the hands predatory neighbours.

Some officials soldier on, employing all means available to reverse the quickly worsening situation. Yet others increasingly sacrifice the public good to personnel gain and self-interest—using whatever power they retain to increase their own wealth and security at the expense of others. Not surprisingly, charges of state corruption increase and opposition forces are strengthened.

As Zefra spirals into ever increasing unrest, news coverage of the tragedy in the making (growing insurrection) intensifies and calls for UN intervention proliferate.

The growing anti-Western climate promoted by challenger groups nevertheless ensures that the besieged regime is hesitant to seek the world body's assistance. And increasing levels of violence within Zefra itself raise concerns within key member-states that the potential costs of intervention may well exceed what western publics may be willing to bear for the sake of humanity.

Still, fears of a wider conflict—perhaps enveloping the entire region itself, and the massive refugee flows likely to attend such a prospect—ensure that incentives for action are not only sustained, but increase. Emerging allegations of FIF's linkages with international organized criminal organizations—some with strong connections to a growing trade in exotic and highly destructive weaponry—intensify international concern. Some claim that the long-running stalemate between the regime and its challengers is poised to shift in favour of the latter—with potential consequences too terrible to contemplate. Accordingly, they claim that intervention is essential.

Yet others continue to advise caution, dismissing such reports as pure rumour and hoping that the uneasy military stalemate between the regime and its challengers will soon bring both parties to the realization that ceasefire and negotiation are the only routes to salvation for Zefra and its people.

Countdown to Intervention

As weeks turn into months, observers nevertheless note the development of what seems to be an uneasy stability within the crumbling nation. While armed clashes continue, their intensity and frequency declines as both sides exhibit a seeming acceptance of an uneasy status quo within a divided country. In some areas, conditions even exhibit a moderate improvement as social and commercial activity re-emerges. Accordingly, international concern over a wider conflagration begins to dissipate—with those suggesting otherwise increasingly labelled as excessively alarmist.

Still, enduring pockets of unrest and armed violence remain a source of unease. As the days progress, substantial evidence of reconciliation between the regime and its opponents is nowhere to be found. And despite pockets of relative prosperity in some areas, conditions within the society as a whole continue to deteriorate. Increasingly, the relative calm characterizing the relationship between the regime and its challengers appears less a bellwether of "draw-down" than a possible lull before a coming storm.

ANNEX B—
Fictional Writing Overview

AN OVERVIEW OF FICTIONAL WRITING AND THE CANADIAN ARMY OF THE FUTURE

Major Andrew B. Godefroy, CD Ph.D.

There is an axiom that states all but war is simulation. If true, perhaps among the oldest forms of simulation is literary fiction, a flexible tool that has allowed generations of writers to speculate what past wars may have looked like as well as what future war may look like. Yet whether it is counter-factual "what if?" history or alternative "what the . . . ?" future theory, literary fiction allows both individuals and organizations to investigate ideas, themes, events and outcomes that perhaps otherwise could not have occurred in real life.

As with war gaming, modeling and simulation, military fictional writing allows defence organizations to stimulate interest and debate in past, present and potential future conflicts. Whether it is the application of current tactics or the possibilities of some future concept, fictional narratives may provide a descriptively detailed illustration of virtually any possible scenario within any context. Most importantly, literary fiction serves as a record of possible decisions and is often the first step in bringing future army capabilities to fruition.

Literary fiction and illustrative narratives depicting the Canadian Army began appearing at the end of the nineteenth century. In 1883, Ralph 'Centennius' produced a pamphlet titled *The Dominion*, in which he predicted the state of Canada and the nature of warfare circa 1983. This was followed six years later by W.H.C. Lawrence's *The Storm of '92: A Grandfather's Tale Told in 1932.*[203] A fictional memoir that portrayed a war between Canada and the United States in 1892, Lawrence's book described in detail hypothetical actions between American forces and Canadian militia, the latter of which held the invaders at bay until reinforced by colonial units from across the British Empire. Although not initiated by the Department of Militia and Defence, it was perhaps the first work of fiction dealing with future military "what if?" situations ever published in Canada.

The South African War (1899-1902) provided the next opportunity for literary fiction to play a role in future army concepts. The publication of "The Defence of

---

[203.] W.H.C. Lawrence. *The Storm of '92: A Grandfather's Tale Told in 1932.* (Toronto: Sheppard Publishing Company, 1889).

Duffer's Drift" by Captain (later Major General Sir) Ernest Swinton, KBE CB DSO, in 1905 was extremely well received and became required reading for many subsequent generations of young officers.[204] Set at a river choke point on some generic veldt anywhere in the Transvaal, the story's main character, a young and energetic Lieutenant Backsight Forethought, has a series of nightmares in which he loses battle after battle against his Boer adversaries. After each dream, however, a series of lessons are highlighted, and each of these is incorporated into the next battle, which eventually leads Lieutenant Forethought to victory and relief in the final dream.

Although written as a fictional tale, Swinton's aim was to teach tactical lessons as well as generate discussion and debate on the planning and execution of operations. He noted specifically in his foreword:

This tale of a dream is dedicated to the "gilded Popinjays" and "hired assassins" of the British nation, especially those who are now knocking at the door, to wit the very junior. It embodies some recollections of things actually done and undone in South Africa, 1899–1902. It is hoped that its fantastic guise may really help to emphasize the necessity for the practical application of some very old principles, and assist to an appreciation of what may happen when they are not applied, even on small operations. This practical application has often been lost sight of in the stress of the moment, with dire results, quite unrealized until the horrible instant of actual experience. Should this tale, by arousing the imagination, assist to prevent in the future even one such case of disregard of principles, it will not have been written in vain. The dreams are not anticipations, but merely a record of petty experiences against one kind of enemy in one kind of country only, with certain deductions based thereupon. But from these, given the conditions, it is not difficult to deduce the variations suitable for other countries, or for those occasions when a different foe with different methods of fighting and different weapons has to be met.[205]

"The Defence of Duffer's Drift" set a new precedent for literary fiction in military professional development. The Canadian Army adopted the practice internally during the two World Wars, and continued to publish fictional scenarios in its professional journals during the Cold War era.

Early themes (1945-1960) focused on the transformation of Canada's Army force structure, the adaptation of land forces to the atomic battlefield, and the integration of new technologies into the soldier of tomorrow. As strategic defence concepts transitioned from a policy of mutually assured nuclear

---

[204.] Maj-Gen. Sir Earnest Swinton, "The Defence of Duffer's Drift," *The British Infantry Journal*, (April 1905).

[205.] Ibid.

destruction to one of flexible conventional response in the 1960s, however, thoughts on the future employment of ground forces likewise changed focus.

Towards the 1980s, a possible Third World War fought largely in the European theatre was the center of considerable fictional army narrative, including the publication of two major DND documents detailed below. Interestingly, the 1990s witnessed few such novelizations of Canada's army in a future war, perhaps due to the expected arrival of the post-Cold War peace dividend or the unexpected and unpredictable nature of the New World Order. Whatever the case, debate on future concepts laid largely dormant until very recently.

Early articles appearing in Canadian service literature came from both internal and allied sources. In November 1949, the newly created *Canadian Army Journal* published an article titled, "The Infantry of 1965" that described in considerable detail and with conceptual drawings the outfitting and employment of future ground forces.[206] Focusing heavily on a future defined by atomic warfare, the article suggested, "The main role of infantry in atomic warfare will be to put out of action the enemy atomic bombing bases."[207] The author, H.H. Bryan, also noted that, "Future [land] forces will, then, consist predominantly of infantry, which will be entirely airborne."[208] He also offered that the fast pace of future warfare would ensure that the three-battalion battle group, not the division, would constitute the primary unit of employment in future operations. Finally, Bryan predicted that advanced headquarters close to the front line troops was necessary in any future air-land operation, and that large-scale divisional level static headquarters would likely all but completely disappear from the battlefield.

Bryan also made a number of observations about the future individual soldier. He argued, "The 1965 infantryman will be as familiar with the air vehicle as the truck is to his counterpart today."[209] He suggested that future troops would employ lighter personal equipment, choose agility over endurance, use a helmet that would protect the head from radioactivity, and wear a battle suit that was self-sealing and could be used either at high-altitude or underwater as required. He also predicted that small wireless personal communications, improved preserved rations, and the retention of the grenade and ballistic weapons would shape the soldier of 1965. His final comment that, "within the next two decades the overburdened, plodding, private of the line, with his clumsy boots and cheap contractors clothing, will have disappeared from the scene," unfortunately was

---

[206] H.H. Bryan. "The Infantry of 1965", *Canadian Army Journal*, Vol.2:11 (November 1949), 16-19.

[207] Ibid, 16.

[208] Ibid, 16.

[209] Ibid, 17.

inaccurate, and even today the Canadian Army still faces the challenge of lightening loads and improving clothing for its land forces.

The following year (1950) another article predicting a possible future for the land force appeared in the *Canadian Army Journal*. Authored anonymously by "One of Them," the short fictional scenario described the future visit of the Colonel-in-Chief of the Royal Underground Light Infantry (RULI) to his troops stationed at one of the major army bases in Canada in 1963. Perhaps meant as a criticism of the changing army force structure of the period, the conversation between the C-in-C and the Commanding Officer (CO) highlighted the disintegration of the traditional infantry unit of the Second World War period as specialized trades like signals, transport, pioneering, logistics and anti-armour were removed and placed entirely within their own branches. Although this process slowly began during the Second World War, many tactical support functions remained within the infantry regiment or were directly attached to its command. The author apparently felt that the Canadian Army of the future would consist of numerous specialized branches and services with very little integration or convergence, leaving future infantry battalions extremely isolated and unsupported. Fortunately this prediction did not bear serious fruit, although it demonstrated once again that the Army was trying to conceive the shape of its own existence ten plus years into the future.

Canadian Army future fiction appeared less frequently during the 1960s and 1970s with no significant internal documents being produced for general consumption. However, during this period the public became engaged once more in the exercise of forecasting. Bruce Powe foreshadowed the subsequent FLQ Crisis with his 1968 publication of Killing Ground: The Canadian Civil War.[210] Described as "a war game novel, a projection of events based on assumptions which may or may not become valid in actual experience," it was perhaps the first detailed examination of what might be required of the Canadian Army in aiding the civil power under emergency measures in a modern conflict.

Increased concerns during the late 1970s that a NATO-Warsaw Pact war might erupt in Europe during the early 1980s instigated several fictional tales both in print and on film. Most notable in this genre to the Canadian Army was the 1978 public release of *The Third World War: August 1985*, by General Sir John Hackett and other NATO analysts. While admitting that "the authors make their conviction clear that the only forecast which can be offered with confidence about the future is that nothing will happen exactly as they have shown it," the story presented a remarkably detailed and very plausible fictional narrative of

---

[210.] Bruce Powe. *Killing Ground: The Canadian Civil War*. (Toronto: Peter Martin Associates, 1968). Powe served in the Canadian Army overseas from 1943 to 1945, and later became a prominent layer and public servant.

how just such a war might unfold. At close to 500 pages, *The Third World War* was presented as a history of the war written shortly after its conclusion. It discussed both causes and aftermath, and included—albeit briefly—what roles Canada's military might have played as part of the NATO forces in Europe. A second volume, titled *The Third World War: The Untold Story*, appeared in 1982 and served as both an update and as an expansion on events the authors were unable to explore in depth in the first book.

Hackett's work was closely followed by both American and Canadian tactical-level studies of fighting on the West German plains. Of note in the American public literature were *Red Storm Rising* by Tom Clancy and Larry Bond (1986) and *Team Yankee* by Harold Coyle (1987). In Canada, Force Mobile Command (FMC) initiated two fictional studies of Canadian Army operations in this type of conflict. In 1984 DND released the first illustrated narrative, First Clash, written by Major (ret'd) Kenneth Macksey, MC.[211] A former officer of the Royal Tank Regiment with service as a troop commander in Normandy in 1944, Macksey used the literary technique to provide Canadian commanders serving in Western Europe in 1984 with a better mental image of the phases of a battle group's approach and involvement against a Soviet Tank Division in a fictional battle. Focusing on company groups and combat teams, readers shadow the life of character Lieutenant Colonel Doug Tinker, Commanding Officer of 3rd Battalion, Royal Canadian Regiment Battle Group, as he fights a defensive battle against Major-General Gregor Samsonov's 1st Guards Tank Division on the Buhl Plateau. Macksey republished the highly successful study into the public domain with Sterling Publishing Company in 1985.

Though not necessarily a portrayal of future technology it was designed to be a training aid with the purpose of creating a mental image of what Canadian soldiers at war in Western Europe might look like. Overall, the narrative was very well received by the army and considered essential reading for junior and mid-level leadership and command. The success of *First Clash* prompted the publication of a successor novel by Macksey in 1989/1990 titled *Counterstroke*.[212] Although not specifically a sequel to *First Clash* it had the same aim of providing a mental image of land forces in future battles and was delivered in almost the exact same format and style. In *Counterstroke*, the Soviet adversary was replaced by the more generic and at the time politically correct Fantasian Army, however it was immediately obvious that the two were one and the same, given that the

---

[211.] Kenneth J. Macksey. *First Clash*. (Ottawa: DND Publication B-GL-309-006/FT-001, 15 February 1984). The publication was prepared by Force Mobile Command Headquarters. A slightly modified version was subsequently published as, *First Clash: Canadians in World War Three*. (Toronto: Stoddard Publishing, 1984, 1985).

[212.] Kenneth J. Macksey. *Counterstroke*. (Ottawa: DND Publication B-GL-309-007/FT-001, 1989/90).

ground fought over was still Germany.

Still, there were other differences within the story. *First Clash* employed the Canadian Army organizations and equipment, as they existed in 1984, whereas *Counterstroke* was based on the notional Corps 86 ideas and its associated doctrine.[213] The novel also provides the caveat in its introduction that "the reader should be aware that many of the organizations and equipment described do not exist and may never exist.[214] Regardless, like *First Clash* the publication achieved its aim of providing a mental image and stimulating interest in army operations through a fictional yet realistic portrayal of events in battle.

There has not been a lengthy fictional assessment of the future army *within* DND since the publication of *Counterstroke* in 1989/90.[215] Although numerous short vignettes appeared discussing the impact of various technologies within DND publications throughout the 1990s,[216] no author undertook a more detailed speculation of Canada's future Army across the entire spectrum of operations. The nature of the period was surely a factor: high operational tempo combined with a wide diversity in mission tasks and geographic locations. Though some believed that Canada would continue to prepare for a future large-scale high-intensity war, others more accurately predicted that the Balkan "sideshow" would soon assume centre stage for Canada's Army. The publication of the defence White Paper in 1994 also provided little detailed insight as to what the future might hold, except to suggest that the Canadian Army could find itself doing pretty much anything, anywhere.

In 1997 the Canadian Army formed the Directorate of Land Strategic Concepts in Kingston, Ontario. Assigned the mission of conceiving Canada's Army of the future, the directorate's mandate was ideally suited for the creation of a new fictional story predicting how Canada's army might live and fight during the mid 21st century. In 2003, DLSC began work on *Crisis in Zefra*, a story set in a failed state somewhere in Saharan Africa that follows a typical Canadian infantry section

---

[213] Corps 86 was the name for a popular notional order of battle that included the fictitious 10 Canadian Mechanized Brigade Group (CMBG).

[214] Ibid, preface, iii.

[215] The foreword of *Counterstroke* suggests that a third volume was then in preparation, but very likely the end of the Cold War and the subsequent review of Canadian defence policy in 1994 resulted in the termination of this work.

[216] For example see Capt. Andrew B. Godefroy. "The Modern Umbrella: Space Assets As a Force Multiplier in Land Warfare", *The Army Doctrine and Training Bulletin: Canada's Professional Journal on Army Issues*. Vol. No.2 (November 1998), 18-22. This article begins by highlighting the potential future employment of space-derived information in ground operations.

on an atypical patrol.

Considering that no one predicted in the late 1980s that the Canadian Army would be fully committed to asymmetric wars and peacekeeping in places like the Balkans and Afghanistan during the 1990s and beyond, the need for speculation, thought and most importantly informed debate on the future of the Canadian Army continues to be critical to today's planning for the future. One means of encouraging these activities is through the employment of speculative fiction. This publication, *Crisis in Zefra*, builds on over a century of Canadian Army tradition of looking ahead, and offers soldiers at all levels with food for thought, consideration, and debate. Based on precedent, *Crisis in Zefra* is an invaluable tool to help shape our successors.

GLOSSARY OF TERMS²¹⁷

Ad-hoc Network	A mobile ad-hoc network (MANET) is a self-configuring network of mobile routers (and associated hosts) connected by wireless links—the union of which forms an arbitrary topology. The routers are free to move randomly and organise themselves arbitrarily; thus, the network's wireless topology may change rapidly and unpredictably. Such a network may operate in a standalone fashion, or may be connected to the larger Internet.
Aggregator	A news aggregator is a piece of software or a remotely hosted service that periodically reads a set of news sources, in one of several XML-based formats (RSS or Atom), finds the new bits, and displays them on a single page. There are three primary types: desktop news aggregators, online news aggregators, and server side aggregators.
Augmented Reality	Augmented reality (AR) is a field of computer research that deals with the combination of real-world and computer generated data. At present, most AR research is concerned with the use of live video imagery, which is digitally processed and "augmented" by the addition of computer-generated graphics. Advanced research includes the use of motion tracking data, fiducial (target) marker recognition using machine vision, and the construction of controlled environments containing any number of sensors and actuators.
Electromagnetic Pulse	In telecommunications and warfare, the term electromagnetic pulse (EMP) has the following meanings:
.	The electromagnetic radiation from an explosion

---

^{217.} Definitions extracted from the *Wikipedia*—a Web-based free content encyclopedia that may be read and edited by anyone. It has 195 independent language editions sponsored by the non-profit Wikimedia Foundation. Entries on traditional encyclopedic topics exist alongside those on almanac, gazetteer and current events topics. It is "an effort to create and distribute a free encyclopedia of the highest possible quality to every single person on the planet in their own language." (http://en.wikipedia.org/wiki/Main_Page)

(especially a nuclear explosion) or an intensely fluctuating magnetic field caused by Compton-recoil electrons and photoelectrons from photons scattered in the materials of the electronic or explosive device or in a surrounding medium. The resulting electric and magnetic fields may couple with electrical/electronic systems to produce damaging current and voltage surges. The effects are usually not noticeable beyond the blast radius unless the device is nuclear or specifically designed to produce an electromagnetic shockwave.

A broadband, high-intensity, short-duration burst of electromagnetic energy.

In the case of a nuclear detonation, the electromagnetic pulse consists of a continuous frequency spectrum. Most of the energy is distributed throughout the lower frequencies between 3 Hz and 30 kHz.

Electronic Paper

Electronic paper, or e-paper, is a technology that allows the text on a piece of paper to be re-written. The "paper" is actually made of organic electronics that use conductive plastic, which contains tiny balls that respond to an electric charge, changing the page in much the same way that pixels change on a computer monitor. Electronic paper was developed in order to overcome some of the limitations of computer monitors. For example, the backlighting of monitors is hard on the human eye, whereas electronic paper reflects light just like normal paper. It is easier to read at an angle than flat screen monitors. Because it is made of plastic, electronic paper has the potential to be flexible. It is light and potentially inexpensive.

Flash Mob

Flash mob is a group of people who assemble suddenly in a public place, do something unusual or notable, and then disperse. They are usually organized with the help of the Internet or other digital communications networks.

Fuel Cell

A fuel cell is an electrochemical device similar to a battery, but differing from the latter in that it is designed for continuous replenishment of the reactants consumed; i.e. it produces electricity from an external fuel supply as opposed to the limited internal energy storage capacity of a battery. Typical reactants used in a fuel cell are hydrogen on the anode side and oxygen on the cathode side (a hydrogen cell). In contrast, conventional batteries consume solid reactants and, once these reactants are depleted, must be discarded, recharged with electricity by running the chemical reaction backwards, or, at least in theory, having their electrodes replaced. Typically in fuel cells, reactants flow in and reaction products flow out, and continuous long-term operation is feasible virtually as long as these flows are maintained.

Globalization

Globalization is a term used to describe the changes in societies and the world economy that are the result of dramatically increased trade and cultural exchange. In specifically economic contexts, it refers almost exclusively to the effects of trade, particularly trade liberalization or "free trade." Globalization has become identified with a number of trends, most of which may have developed since World War II. These include greater international movement of commodities, money, information and people; and the development of technology, organizations, legal systems and infrastructures to allow this movement. The actual existence of some of these trends is debated.

- Increase in international trade at a faster rate than the growth in the world economy

- Increase in international flow of capital including foreign direct investment

- Greater trans-border data flow, using such technologies such as the Internet, communication satellites and telephones

- Greater international cultural exchange, for example through the export of Hollywood and Bollywood movies.

- Some argue that even terrorism has undergone globalization. Terrorists now have attacked places all over the world.

- Spreading of multiculturalism and better individual access to cultural diversity, with on the other hand, some reduction in diversity through assimilation, hybridization, Westernization, Americanization or Sinosization of cultures.

- Erosion of national sovereignty and national borders through international agreements leading to organizations like the WTO and OPEC

- Greater international travel and tourism

- Greater immigration, including illegal immigration

- Development of global telecommunications infrastructure

- Development of a global financial systems

- Increase in the share of the world economy controlled by multinational corporations

- Increased role of international organizations such as WTO, WIPO, and IMF that deal with international transactions

- Increase in the number of standards applied globally; e.g. copyright laws

LIDAR

LIDAR (light detection and ranging or laser imaging detection and ranging) is a technology that determines distance to an object or surface using laser pulses. Like the similar radar technology, which uses radio waves instead of light, the range to an object is determined by measuring the time delay between transmission of a pulse and detection of the reflected signal. The acronym LADAR (LAser Detection And Ranging) for elastic backscatter lidar systems is mainly used in military context. The term laser radar is also in use but somewhat misleading as laser light and not radio waves are used.

Koran

The Qur'an (Arabic al-qur'an ?????????; its literal meaning is "the recitation" and is often called "Al Qu'ran Al Karim": "The Noble Qu'ran", also transliterated as Quran, Koran, and less commonly Alcoran) is the holy book of Islam. Muslims believe that the Qur'an is the literal word of God and the culmination of God's revelation to mankind, revealed to the Prophet Muhammad over a period of 23 years by the Angel Jibreel (Gabriel). The Qur'an consists of 114 suras (chapters) with a total of 6,236 ayat (verses; the exact number of ayat is disputed, not due to content dispute but due to different methods of counting). The

Qur'an retells stories of many of the people and events recounted in Jewish and Christian sacred books (Torah, Bible) and devotional literature (Apocrypha, Midrash), although it differs in many details. Well-known Biblical characters such as Adam, Noah, Abraham, Moses, Jesus and John the Baptist are mentioned in the Qur'an as Prophets of Islam.

Malware

Malware or "malicious software" is any software developed for the purpose of doing harm to a computer system. Two common types of malware are viruses and worms. These types of programs have in common that they are both able to self-replicate: they can spread (possibly modified) copies of themselves. Not every program that copies itself is a virus or worm; for instance, backup software may copy itself to other media as part of a system backup. To be classified as a virus or worm, at least some of these copies have to be able to replicate themselves too, such that the virus or worm can propagate itself. The difference between a virus and a worm is that a worm operates more or less independently of other files, whereas a virus depends on hosts to spread itself.

Minder

An information appliance (IA) is any device that can process information, signals, graphics, animation, video and audio, and can exchange such information with another IA or minder device. Typical devices could be smartphones, smartcards, PDAs, and so on. Digital cameras, ordinary cellular phones, set-top boxes, and LCD TVs are not information appliances unless they become capable of communications and information functions. Information appliances may overlap in definition and are sometimes referred to as smart devices, mobile devices, wireless devices, internet appliances, web appliances, handhelds, handheld devices or smart handheld devices.

The essential characteristics of a tactically decisive Army are:

Moblog (mobile weblog)

A mobile weblog, or moblog, consists of content posted to the Internet from a mobile or portable device, such as a cellular phone or PDA. Moblogs generally involve technology which allows publishing from a mobile device. Much of the earliest development of moblogs occurred in Japan, among the first countries in the world where camera phones (portable phones with built-in cameras) were widely commercially available.

Nanotechnology   Nanotechnology comprises any technological developments on the nanometer scale, usually 0.1 to 100 nm. (One nanometer equals one thousandth of a micrometer or one millionth of a millimetre.) The term has sometimes been applied to any microscopic technology. The term nanotechnology is often used interchangeably with molecular nanotechnology (also known as "MNT"), a hypothetical, advanced form of nanotechnology believed to be achievable at some point in the future. Molecular nanotechnology includes the concept of mechanosynthesis. The term nanoscience is used to describe the interdisciplinary field of science devoted to the advancement of nanotechnology. The size scale of nanotechnology makes it susceptible to quantum-based phenomena, leading to often-counterintuitive results. These nanoscale phenomena include quantum size effects and molecular forces such as van der Waals forces. Furthermore, the vastly increased ratio of surface area to volume opens new possibilities in surface-based science, such as catalysis. Radical nanotechnology is a term given to sophisticated nanoscale machines operating on the molecular scale. By the countless examples found in biology it is currently known that radical nanotechnology would be possible to construct. Many scientists today believe that it is likely that evolution has made optimized biological nanomachines with close to optimal performance possible for nanoscale machines, and that radical nanotechnology thus would need to made by biomimetic principles. However, it has been suggested by K Eric Drexler that radical nanotechnology can be made by mechanical engineering like principles. Drexler's idea of a diamondoid molecular nanotechnology is currently controversial and it remains to be seen what future developments will bring.

Remailer   An anonymous remailer is a server computer which receives messages with embedded instructions on where to send them next, and which forwards them without revealing where they originally came from. There are Cypherpunk anonymous remailers, Mixmaster anonymous remailers, and nym servers, among others, which differ in how they work, in the policies they adopt, and in the type of attack on anonymity of email they can (are intended to) resist. Remailing as discussed in this article applies to emails intended for particular recipients, not the general public. Anonymity in the latter case is more easily addressed by using any of several methods of anonymous publication.

Smart Dust   Smartdust is a network of tiny wireless microelectromechanical sensors (MEMS), robots, or devices, installed with wireless communications that can detect anything from light and temperature, to vibrations, etc. The devices are also called motes and are intended to shrink down to the size of a grain of sand, or even a dust particle. Each device contains sensors, computing circuits, bidirectional wireless communications technology and a power supply. Motes would gather data, run computations and communicate using two-way band radio with other motes at distances approaching 1,000 feet (300 metres). When clustered together, they automatically create highly flexible, low-power networks with applications ranging from climate control systems to entertainment devices that interact with information appliances.

Smart Mob   Smart mob is a concept introduced by Howard Rheingold in his book Smart Mobs: The Next Social Revolution. A recently established form of social coordination made possible by using modern technology, such as the Internet and wireless devices like mobile phones and PDAs, a "smart mob" is a group that, contrary to the usual connotations of a mob, behaves intelligently or efficiently because of its exponentially-increasing network links. Essentially, the smart mob is a practical implementation of collective intelligence. According to Rheingold, examples of smart mobs are the street protests organized by the anti-globalization movement. Another example is the text messages that were sent in the Philippines, which are thought to be partly responsible for the demonstration that ousted former President Joseph Estrada. Examples of such a text message might read "wear black to mourn the death of democracy," "expect there to be rumbles" and "go to ESDA."

Three-Block War

The three-block war was a term first coined by General Charles Krulak, the 31st Commandant of the United States Marine Corps. On the first block of the three-block war, the Army could be required to deliver humanitarian aid or assist others in doing that. On the second, stabilization or peace support operations may be required and on the third, the Army might be engaged in a high-intensity fight. The Army must be ready to conduct these operations simultaneously and very close to one another. The Army must be prepared to conduct them in large urban centres and complex terrain.

Vetronics

Vetronics refers to the integrated electrical and electronic systems aboard a vehicle. The domain includes vehicle control subsystems, diagnostics, electrical power, displays, communications, and all payload electronics.

BIBLIOGRAPHY

Army. *Advancing With Purpose: The Army Strategy*. (Ottawa: May 2002).

Army. *Purpose Defined: The Force Employment Concept for the Army: One Army, One Team, One Vision*. (Ottawa: March 2004).

Directorate of Land Strategic Concepts. *Future Force: Concepts for Future Army Capabilities*. (Kingston: 2003).

Gizewski, P. and Horn, LCol B. eds. *Towards the Brave New World: Canada's Army in the 21st Century*. (Kingston: 2003).

CONTRIBUTORS

Crisis in Zefra is a product of the ongoing DLSC Futures Project. Initiated in late 2003, it evolved through several phases of research, development, illustration and story writing to complete the final manuscript. Many people contributed to the success of the project as follows:

DLSC Research Team

Colonel Guy Maillet

Lieutenant Colonel Kenneth Faulkner

Lieutenant Colonel David Galea

Lieutenant Colonel Bernd Horn

Lieutenant Colonel Michael Maurer

Lieutenant Colonel Robert Williams

Major Andrew Godefroy

Major John Sheahan

Mr. Fred Cameron

Mr. Peter Gizewski

Mr. Regan Reshke

Zefra Project Coordinator

Major Andrew Godefroy

Author

Mr. Karl Schroeder

Illustrator

Mr. Kalman Andrasofszky

INDEX